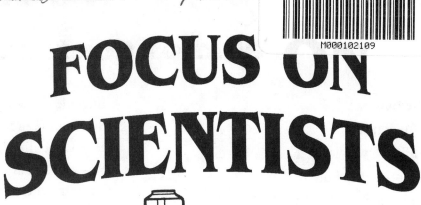

FOCUS ON SCIENTISTS

Authors:
Mary Ellen Sterling, M. Ed.

Illustrators:
Kathy Bruce

Cover Design:
Amy LasCola

Cover Artist:
Blanca Apodaca La Bounty

Editor:
Karen Goldfluss, M.S. Ed.

Senior Editor:
Sharon Coan, M.S. Ed.

Art Direction:
Elayne Roberts
Darlene Spivak

Product Manager:
Phil Garcia

Imaging:
Paula Spence

Publishers:
Rachelle Cracchiolo, M.S. Ed.
Mary Dupuy Smith, M.S. Ed.

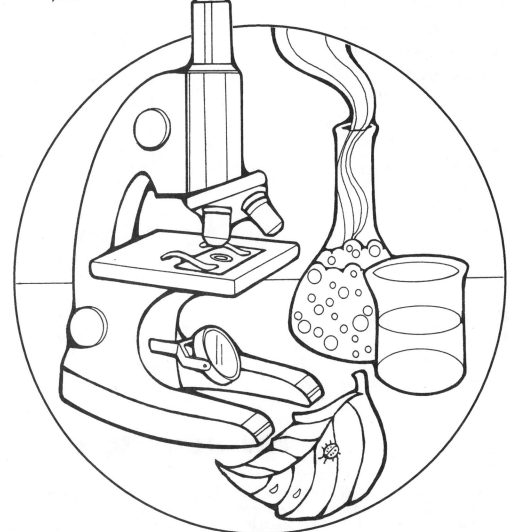

Teacher Created Materials, Inc.
P.O. Box 1040
Huntington Beach, CA 92647
©*1994 Teacher Created Materials, Inc.*
Made in U.S.A.

ISBN 1-55734-493-0

Table of Contents

Introduction

Focus on Scientists is a blend of important contributors whose discoveries, experiments, and inventions have enriched and improved our present way of life. Some scientists named in this book lived in ancient times; others are from a more modern era. Many of the scientists here are world-famous, but others are not as well-known. Yet they all share one thing in common. Each of them has made a significant impact in the field of science and on our world.

One purpose of this book is to acquaint students with some of the people who have touched their lives in subtle but significant ways. A secondary intention is to highlight the role of women in science and to present a cross-section of men and women from various cultures and backgrounds. Finally, scientists from all three fields of science, Earth, Life, and Physical, are represented in *Focus on Scientists*.

Within the three science areas of this unit are biographies of selected scientists. Following the biography pages are related activities and experiments, along with a listing of related reading material (tradebooks, fiction, periodicals, etc.). Activity pages follow each biography and serve to enrich the students' knowledge and appreciation of the scientists' contributions.

This fine resource will enable you to present some fascinating and motivational information to students. It is hoped that the inspiring stories of the men and women on these 112 pages and their amazing accomplishments will inspire students to explore science topics on their own.

Using the Pages

How you use the pages in this book depends on any number of factors which may include school district curriculum guidelines, learning levels of the students, personal teaching styles and goals, and how well a topic blends with a particular theme.

The following descriptions of the book's features are intended to help you get the most from each page.

Sections

The scientists presented in this book are categorized by the science areas they most represent. The book is divided into three sections: Earth Scientists, Life Scientists, and Physical Scientists. Choose scientists from the science area emphasized in your curriculum.

Biographies

The biographies provided can be read aloud to students, copied for group or individual student use, or used for your reference.

Create a book of biographies for class use. Copy each biography, punch holes along one side of the papers, and assemble them into a three-ring binder. Add dividers labeled Earth Scientists, Life Scientists, and Physical Scientists. Write and add biographies of any other scientists that you study.

Themes

To focus on a particular theme, such as Women Scientists or Twentieth Century Scientists, refer to the lists on pages 10, 42, and 79. Write each scientist's name on a separate index card and place the cards in a paper bag. Have each student or pair of students draw a name. Provide them with a choice of activities to complete. Students can share what they have learned with the whole class or in small groups.

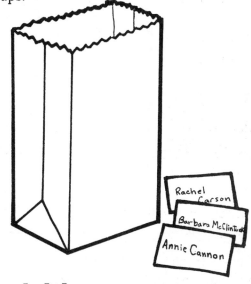

Activities

Suggested activities follow each biography and are provided so that you may vary the way lessons are presented. Choose those which best suit your classroom needs and adapt them to fit your students' abilities and your teaching style. Another option is to allow students to choose their activities.

Activity pages are written to accommodate a number of learning levels. Determine which of these activities may be suitable for your students, and feel free to alter the directions if necessary. Also, you may pair or group students to complete a project.

A brief bibliography follows the activities. It provides a selection of related references available to teachers and students. Check your school, public, or university library for other titles.

A Scientific Overview

Science is an organized system or body of knowledge based on observations, experiments, and accurate thinking. The people who perform these observations and experiments are called scientists. These brave pioneers pave the way for those who follow by applying ideas in new and unique ways. A scientist must possess a good imagination, formulate original ideas, and be unafraid to explore the unknown.

The field of science can be divided into three main areas — Earth, Life, and Physical. Each of these three areas can be further subdivided into the scientific studies described below.

Earth Sciences

Geology is the study of the earth's history and structure. It includes the study of fossils, both plant and animal, and theories of the earth's evolution.

Meteorology is the study of weather conditions, climate, and ways to predict weather.

Oceanography explores both plant and animal life of the ocean, mapping the ocean floor, and studying ocean currents.

Geography is the study of the surface of the earth. It includes surveying and mapping, examining the physical features of the earth, and observing the distribution of life.

Astronomy involves the study of the sun and other stars, the moon, and the planets.

Life Sciences

Zoology is the scientific study of animal life. It also encompasses anatomy, physiology, genetics, and animal behavior.

Ecology is closely related to zoology. Scientists in the field study plants and animals in relation to their environment.

Botany studies the behavior and functioning of plants.

Physical Sciences

Chemistry is the study of the nature, composition, and properties of substances and their transformations, specifically of elements, compounds, atoms, and molecules.

Physics is the study of matter and motion and their energy. Some main areas of physics are light, heat, sound, mechanics, electricity, and magnetism.

Although there are additional divisions and subdivisions within the field of science, the areas of science described above represent the studies of the scientists cited in this book.

The Scientific Method

The definition of the term science states that it is an organized body of knowledge. Information is stored according to predetermined guidelines and a systematic method. In order to track and gather this information in an orderly manner, scientists employ what is commonly known as the scientific method.

To use the scientific method, scientists follow a specific series of problem-solving steps. The central steps in this process are outlined below.

Problem-Solving Steps

1. **Identify and make a clear statement of the problem.** (e.g., Do plants need light in order to grow?)

2. **Gather information about the problem.** (Use a variety of sources including textbooks, trade books, journals, films, videotapes, and computer programs.)

3. **Formulate a hypothesis or a proposed solution to the problem.** A hypothesis about plant growth might be stated, "I think plants do need light in order to grow."

4. **Test the hypothesis by making observations.** This can be done through experiments or by using any combination of the five senses. (e.g., Obtain two identical plants. Place one in a closet and the other in a sunny spot. Care for each the same way. Illustrate and write about daily observations.)

5. **Draw a conclusion.** After the experiment has been completed, write a statement which sums up what happened and reflects upon the hypothesis. (e.g., The plant in the sun thrived while the plant in the closet wilted and lost its color. My conclusion is that plants do need light in order to grow.)

While this method is helpful in solving problems, it is not foolproof. Scientists know they must make careful observations and be objective in drawing conclusions. It is easy to be influenced by what others think, to use information in the wrong way, or to answer a question according to how we would like it to be answered. Guide students through this thinking process with the activity on page 6. Then, group the students and have them use the scientific method to solve any of the problems presented on that same page.

Thinking Like a Scientist

Use this activity to guide students through the scientific method. Review the five steps of the method before sharing the example below.

1. **Ask a question.** Questions that prompt an investigation are often the result of one's observation of a situation or event. Based on the observation, an inquisitive mind seeks the reason, or "why", which leads to an investigation of the problem. Consider the following example: When you returned from a month-long visit at your grandparents' house, you noticed that your two plants were greener and fuller than before you left for vacation. During your absence your older brother tended the plants. Your question might be, "Why did the plants grow greener and fuller while I was gone?"

2. **Gather information about the problem.** This step requires that you search for clues that will help you answer the question. To determine what happened to make plants grow in the example above, you might begin with questions about the plant care-giver, your brother. Did he move the plants or do anything different to them while you were away? Did he allow anyone else to care for the plants? After talking with your brother, you find out that he cared for the plants himself and that he did do some things differently. First, he watered them twice a week. Second, he moved them closer to the sunlight. He did, however, use the same fertilizer you used. Make a chart to help you analyze the information you have gathered.

The Care of My Plants During My Vacation		
Type of Care	**Same**	**Different**
Placement in relation to sunlight		✓
Fertilizer	✓	
Watering schedule		✓

3. **Formulate a hypothesis.** Based on the information gathered, you may form a scientific guess about what happened. For example, you might state, "Moving the plants closer to sunlight and watering them weekly caused the plants to grow greener and fuller."

4. **Test the hypothesis.** Plan an experiment to test your hypothesis. Move one plant back to its pre-vacation position and care for it exactly as you did before. This will be the control plant. Leave the other plant in the sunlight and follow your brother's procedure. This is the experimental plant. Observe both plants for one week.

5. **Draw a conclusion.** Note what happened as a result of the experiment. You might state, "Moving the plant closer to sunlight and watering it twice weekly helped it to grow greener and fuller."

On Your Own _____

Use the problem-solving steps of the scientific method to answer the following questions.

1. Do you eat more food when you are on a sports team than when you are not?

2. Do you watch more television during the weekends than you do on week nights?

3. Are you more alert before or after a fast-food dinner?

4. What type of food does your pet like best?

5. Does your family use more seasonings on burgers or on chicken?

The Discovery Approach

While the scientific method described on page 5 is a valid and useful thinking matrix, it does not fit the needs of all learners. Young children may have difficulty with the abstract concepts involved. Currently, a trend being seen more and more in science education is the discovery approach. Here the students are confronted with selected phenomena and situations. They are then asked to propose problems to be solved and methods of solution.

For example, a student group might be presented with the following array of objects: a ball of clay, nails, small stones, metal coins, washers or sinkers, and a bowl of water. The students are asked if they can make these objects float. From previous experience the students know that the items will sink when placed in the bowl of water. (If they are not sure that the objects will sink or swim, they may experiment at this point to find out.) What can they do to make the items float? Someone in the group may suggest making a small boat using some of the clay. After some trial and error, they will find that placing an object in the clay boat will help it float.

Initially, students may have a difficult time with this lateral thinking, and they may also become easily frustrated, wanting to give up if a solution is not readily found. You must act as a facilitator, encouraging students with guided questions. Ask the students, for example, which of the objects before them can be changed in form. The answer is the clay. Further guide them by asking them what they can do to the clay to get it to float. Someone will probably come to the conclusion that they can make a clay, boat and after some experimentation with the size of the boat, they may get the idea to float the objects in it.

Not only does the discovery approach employ a number of critical thinking skills, it is also conducive to cooperative grouping. An idea is presented to a group, and through discussions and cooperative efforts, a general consensus is reached. No one idea is considered incorrect and everyone's input is encouraged.

For more information about the discovery approach, check with your local school district or teacher-training college. Some science trade books are being written using the discovery method. One fine example is Sandra Markle's *Science Mini-Mysteries* (Atheneum, 1988). Also, several experiments in this book employ the discovery approach. They can be found on the following pages:

Portable Experiments Kits

An easy and fun way to keep students motivated about science is through the use of Portable Experiments Kits. These are kits which you build yourself using easily accessible materials. The kits can then be checked overnight for use by your students. For best results, follow the step-by-step directions below.

1. **Collect a variety of materials.** Enlist parents to contribute these items. A sample letter along with a list of supplies can be found on page 9.

2. **Determine how you want to organize the kits.** Possible containers include plastic boxes, shoe boxes, or zip top storage bags.

3. **Devise a color-coded labeling system.** For example, use green labels and self-stick dots to denote life science experiments; blue labels and self-stick dots to denote earth science, etc.

4. **Number and name each experiment.** A lesson on magnets might have this label:

P-1 Magnets

   The "P" stands for physical sciences. The numeral "1" indicates that it is the first experiment in that section. "Magnets" is the title of the experiment.

5. **Create a master list of all the portable experiments you make.**

Earth	E-1	Making Fossils
	E-2	Weather Vanes
Life	L-1	Making Flea Repellent
	L-2	Growing Pea Plants
Physical	P-1	Magnets
	P-2	Making a Battery

6. **Choose experiments that students can do easily at home.** Make sure that if the experiments require anything not included in the kit, these items are readily available and inexpensive.

7. **Assemble all the materials needed for a specific experiment.** Write clear, concise directions on a sheet of heavy paper. (Make back-up copies and file them.) Laminate the directions sheet. Place the materials into a container. Label each item, including the directions, with an appropriate color-coded self-stick dot. For example, each item for the magnet experiment should have a blue dot with the code "P-1."

8. **Use library pockets and check-out cards to keep track of the kits.** When students check out a kit, store the cards inside a file box.

9. **Store the kits in a specifically designated area.** The area can be anything from a big cardboard box to wooden shelves, but it should be used exclusively for storing the kits.

Activities from this book that would make good portable experiments are noted with a **KIT** symbol.

8

Can you Help?

Dear Parents and Guardians,

One of the goals of our science program is to provide students with hands-on experiences which actively involve their participation. Not only do students enjoy these activities, but they also come away from the experience with a real understanding of the concepts being presented.

With this in mind, we are preparing Portable Experiments Kits. Students will check out these kits to conduct experiments at home. All materials needed to conduct the experiments will be included in the kits. Please provide a receptive ear and listen to your child explain a particular experiment and what was learned. You can reinforce your youngster's learning by encouraging him/her to talk about the experiment results.

To get this program started, we will have to assemble all the items needed for the kits. Please review the following list and send whatever items you can to school.

Thank you for supporting our class and our science program.

Sincerely yours,

wind-up clocks and watches
tagboard or cardboard
magnetic compass
compass (to draw circles)
thick convex lens
thin convex lens
cardboard tubes from foil, etc.
plastic straws
paper plates
small milk cartons
sea shells
petroleum jelly
golf balls; soft balls; tennis balls
darning needles
foam packaging pieces
self-sealing plastic bags
cereal boxes (empty)
fast food buckets
plastic wrap; aluminum foil
plastic margarine cups with lids

funnels	wooden spoons
hot plate	foam meat-packing trays
corks	cooking oil
sugar	magnifying glass
cloth	glass jars with lids
balloons	toothpicks
wire	string; yarn; thread
candles	thumb tacks
mirrors	foam egg cartons
salt	nut grinder
saucepan	rubber tubing
peanuts	plastic cups
rolling pin	paper towels
cornstarch	forks; spoons
tin cans	handkerchief
washers	straight pins

Earth Scientists

Below is a listing of the earth scientists who are represented in this section. Following each name is a brief summary of related information.

Scientist	Area of Study	Country of Origin	Achievement
Benjamin Banneker (1731-1806)	Astronomy	U.S.A.	self-taught; wrote an almanac
Annie Jump Cannon (1863-1941)	Astronomy	U.S.A.	worked at Harvard 40 years; classified over 350,000 stars
Jacques Cousteau (1910-)	Oceanography	France	pioneered underwater exploration; co-invented aqualung
Charles Darwin (1809-1882)	Evolution	Great Britain	formulated theory of evolution by natural selection
Galileo Galilei (1564-1642)	Astronomy and Physics	Italy	discovered laws of falling bodies; observed pendulums
Matthew Henson (1865-1955)	Exploration	U.S.A.	accompanied Peary on 6 Arctic trips; first to walk on North Pole
Maria Mitchell (1818-1889)	Astronomy	U.S.A.	discovered a comet; first female astronomer in America
John Muir (1838-1914)	Environmental Studies	U.S.A.	named father of our national parks; first president of Sierra Club
Joanne Simpson (1923-)	Meteorology	U.S.A.	experimented with cloud seeding and hurricane modifcation
Alexander von Humboldt (1767-1859)	Biogeography	Prussia	made observations which led to science of biogeography

10

Benjamin Banneker

Astronomer

On November 9, 1731, Benjamin Banneker was born to a black freeman and his wife on a farm in Maryland. Young Benjamin was a quick and avid learner. He taught himself to read. Although he attended a Quaker school for a few years, Benjamin Banneker was mostly self-taught.

One example of his special talents can be seen in his clock-making ability. Benjamin was an adult when he first saw a watch; a traveling salesman let him borrow his timepiece. By the end of the week, Benjamin had accurately dismantled and reassembled the watch. He had drawn sketches of every wheel, gear, and spring and went on to make his own watch. Each piece of the watch was carved out of wood.

When Benjamin Banneker was given some crude astrological instruments and some books on astronomy, he taught himself how to use the devices. During his reading, Benjamin discovered errors in the books. Between 1792 and 1802, he published *Benjamin Banneker's Almanack*. It was the second most popular book in America at the time — the *Bible* was first — and it was nicknamed "the poor man's encyclopedia."

Benjamin also used his math skills to help plan the city of Washington, D.C.

Benjamin Banneker's many accomplishments lay dormant for some years after his death in 1806, when scholars unearthed and read his letters, almanacs, and journals. Only then was the scope of his diverse achievements fully realized. Banneker was indeed a man ahead of his time.

Suggested Activities

1. **Mechanical Movement Devices.** Gather some old wind-up clocks and watches and give one to each group of students. Direct students to carefully remove the outer casing so that they can observe the inner workings of the timepiece. Allow groups to do any combination of the following projects.

   • Draw a picture of the gears and wheels as they appear in the timepiece.

   • Compare the groups' diagrams. How are they alike? How are they different?

   • Explain how a clock works. After groups have written their explanations, tell them to compare what they have written from a scientific viewpoint.

   • Identify the simple machines in a mechanical clock (wheel, lever). Make a list of some common tools and gadgets that contain wheels and/or levers.

2. **Clockwise.** Ask students to suggest reasons why clocks run clockwise. After a discussion of reasonable answers, make sure the correct answer has been established. (Before clocks were invented, people used a sundial to tell time. In the Northern hemisphere, shadows cast onto the sundial by the sun rotated in what we now call a clockwise direction. When clocks were built, hands were made to mimic the movement of the shadows.) Read *Anna's Sundial* by Mitsumasa Anno (Philomel Books, 1987) to learn more about sundials.

3. **Make a Sundial.** Provide each group with the following items: one sheet of white tagboard or construction paper, a cardboard 6-inch (15 cm) right triangle, magnetic compass, compass (to draw an arc), and glue. Challenge them to make a sundial using only the items they have been given. (See diagram at right.) **KIT**

   Directions: Fold the triangle's flap; glue it to the center of the paper. With a compass, draw a curved line from two corners of the paper to the triangle's base. Position the magnetic compass so that the tall side of the triangular base points north.

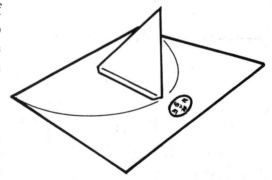

   Extension: Place the completed sundials in the sun. Every hour, mark and label the sun's shadow in its new position as it crosses the curved line. The following day you can use the sundial to tell time.

4. **Stargazing.** Learn about the constellations and how to view them. A very informative book on beginning astronomy is *The Stargazer's Guide to the Galaxy* by Q.L. Pearce (RGA Publishing Group, Inc., 1991).

Teacher References _____

Burns, Marilyn. *Math for Smarty Pants: Or Who Says Mathematicians Have Little Pig Eyes?* Little Brown, 1982.
Software: *Learn About Astronomy.* Tandy/IBM Compatible. DOS 2.0 or Greater. Comedia, Inc. #TC29934.

Student Reading

Conley, Kevin. *Benjamin Banneker: Scientist and Mathematician.* Chelsea House, 1989.
Ferris, Jeri. *What Are You Figuring Now? A Story About Benjamin Banneker.* Carolrhoda Books, 1988.
Moeschl, Richard. *Exploring the Sky: 100 Projects for Beginning Astronomers.* Chicago Review, 1989.

Math Puzzlers

As a scientist and an astronomer, Benjamin Banneker called on his math abilities to solve numerous problems. See how well you can apply your math skills to work the puzzles below. Find a partner to work with you.

1.

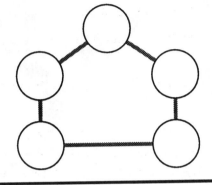

Using only the numerals 1, 2, 3, 4 and 5, write each one in a circle so that no two consecutive numerals are connected. Then, copy the blank figure at left on the back of the paper. Find a different way to fill in the circles using the same numbers. Can you find a third and fourth way?

2.

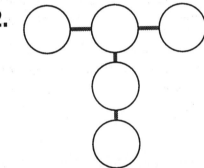

Using only the numerals 1, 2, 3, 4 and 5, write each one in a circle so that the sum of the numbers in each direction is the same. Copy the blank figure at the left on the back of this paper. Figure out a different way to fill in the circles using the same numbers. How many other ways can you find?

3.

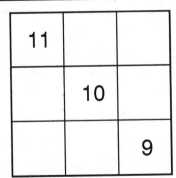

The three numbers shown in the diagram at the left add up to 30 (11 + 10 + 9 = 30). Write a number in each blank square so that every row and column also adds up to 30.

4.

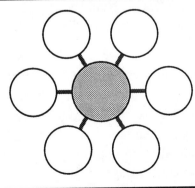

In each of the six small circles of the figure on the left, write a numeral from 1 to 6 so that the difference between two neighboring numbers will be two or less.

Annie Jump Cannon

Astronomer

When Annie Jump Cannon was born on December 18, 1863, the Civil War was raging. It was a time when very few women went beyond grade school or high school. Most women married and raised a family. Career options were limited. But not to Annie Jump Cannon.

Her father was a shipbuilder and his wife's hobby was stargazing. Each night, Mrs. Cannon and Annie would escape to their rooftop observatory. Since Annie was considered a bright student, her teachers convinced her parents to provide her with a higher education. At the age of 16, Annie went to Wellsley College. While she was there, she caught a cold which left her partially deaf. Despite this physical challenge, she graduated and returned home. A few years later, Annie began working in the Harvard Observatory as an assistant to Edward Pickering. He thought women were better suited for the work because they were better observers and more patient with detail.

Annie's work as an assistant consisted of cataloging stars by studying photographic plates. Star pictures were taken by combining photography with telescopes that were equipped with prisms. The resulting pictures showed the differing bands of light produced by each star. After studying the pictures, Annie had to classify the stars. She found it necessary to rearrange the A,B,C classification system that astronomers had been using. The resulting system, which uses the letters O,B,A,F,G,K,M,R,N,and S, is standard even today. Astronomers remember this configuration by reciting this sentence: "Oh, Be A Fine Girl, Kiss Me Right Now, Sweet."

At first Annie worked mostly with available stars or stars that give off unsteady light. Between 1915 and 1924 she produced nine volumes of the _Henry Draper Catalog_, which is a guidebook for astrophysicists even today. This feat made Annie Jump Cannon famous. During her lifetime, she cataloged over 350,000 stars and discovered five novae (stars that suddenly become brighter and then fade). She became the first woman to receive an honorary doctorate from Oxford University. She also won the Draper Medal of the National Academy of Sciences in 1931. Annie Jump Cannon worked until the age of 77.

Suggested Activities

1. **Build a Telescope.** Have the students build their own telescopes following these directions.

   Materials: one thick and one thin convex lens; masking tape; one 14-inch (35 centimeter) long cardboard tube; one 8-inch (20 centimeter) long tube that fits snugly inside the other tube

   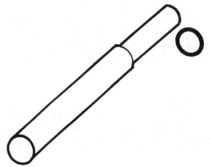

   Procedure: Push the shorter tube halfway into the larger tube. Tape the thick lens to the open end of the smaller tube. Tape the thin lens to the open end of the longer tube. Slide the tubes apart and together to focus on a particular object.

   Discuss the following questions: How do objects appear through the telescope? (upside down) Why do they appear that way? (A mirror or double convex lens has to be placed between the two convex lenses in the tubes in order for objects to appear right side up.)

2. **Prisms.** When Annie Jump Cannon was a little girl, she spent many hours enjoying the dancing rainbows produced by the prisms on her mother's candelabra. Little did she know that one day she would be reading rainbow light from the stars. **KIT**

   Students can construct prisms, or you can demonstrate one for the class, if desired. Necessary materials include a plastic box, water, and a mirror. If the wall is not white, you will need to tape a white sheet of paper on the surface area where the colors will be shown.

   Procedure: Fill the box with water. Slant a mirror in the water so that sunlight strikes the mirror and forms a rainbow on the wall.

3. **Individual Prisms.** Fill a glass with water. Place it on the edge of a table where sunlight can pass through the glass onto a sheet of white paper. You may have to adjust the glass until a rainbow is formed.

4. **Planetarium Visit.** Plan a field trip to a planetarium. If this is not feasible, you may be able to arrange an evening field trip to visit an amateur astronomer and use his/her telescope.

Teacher Reference _____

Emberlin, Diane. *Contributions of Women: Science.* Dillon Press, Inc., 1977.
Ogilvie, Marilyn Bailey. *Women in Science.* MIT Press, 1986.
Yost, Edna. *American Women of Science.* Lippincott, 1943.

Student Reading

Branley, Franklyn. *The Sky Is Full of Stars.* Harper Trophy, 1981.
Sipiera, Paul P. *I Can Be an Astronomer.* Children's Press, 1986.
Veglahn, Nancy. *Women Scientists.* Facts on File, 1991.

Spinning Colors

We see sunlight as colorless, or as "white light." However, when light is passed through a prism, its "unseen" colors can be separated out to form a rainbow pattern called a spectrum. The colors of the spectrum are red, orange, yellow, green, blue, indigo, and violet. Create your own "white light" with the following "Spinning Colors" activity.

Materials: pattern below, reproduced on heavy stock; paints or crayons; scissors; glue; a sharpened pencil; tape

Directions: Use paints or crayons to color in the sections of the circle below as indicated. Cut out the circle. Carefully push the pencil into the center of the circle. Spin the circle quickly and observe what happens.

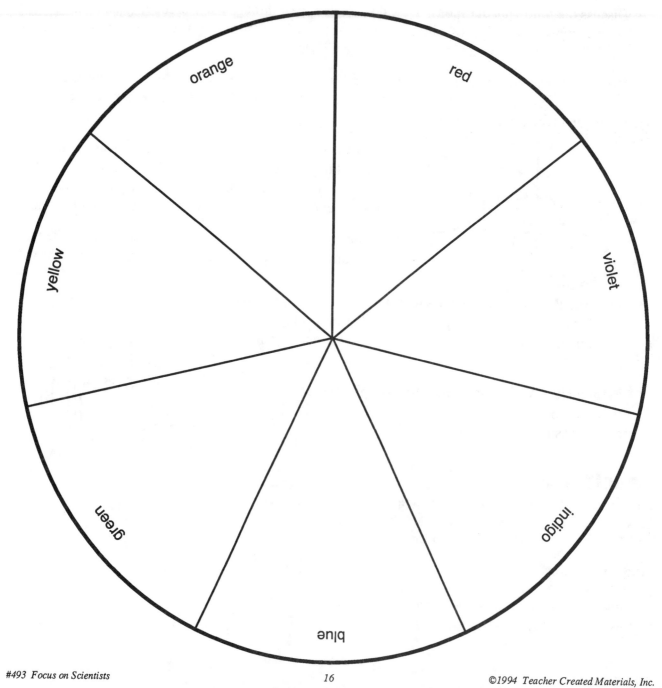

Jacques Cousteau

Oceanologist _____

As a student, Jacques Cousteau was bored by school and was considered to be a troublemaker. An incident in which he broke seventeen windows prompted his parents to enroll him in a strict boarding school.

In 1930, he entered France's naval academy where he graduated second in a class of 1,000.

Jacques joined the French navy after graduation. He was ready to take his flying test when he was injured in an accident and he broke both arms. In order to regain his strength, he turned to swimming.

One day Jacques borrowed a pair of underwater goggles and his life took a new turn. He began to study the ocean and ocean life. In 1942, Jacques Cousteau built an underwater breathing apparatus. The aqualung allowed divers to stay underwater for long periods of time.

In 1950, he bought a sailing vessel and converted it into a floating research laboratory. The famous "Calypso" vessel took Cousteau and his crew on numerous ocean trips. He began to write books and make films to help finance his voyages. An experimental underwater house project was begun; it was called Conshelf 1. Cousteau also taped television shows in 1967; the popular series was called "Undersea World of Jacques Cousteau."

Although Jacques is now in his 80's, he continues to fight tirelessly for the wise use of ocean waters. The amazing man who pioneered underwater exploration also started the Cousteau Society to protect ocean life. Former President Reagan awarded him the 1985 Medal of Freedom. In addition, Cousteau has written a number of books and received Oscars for some of his documentary films.

Suggested Activities

1. **Oceans.** Jacques Cousteau has spent most of his life exploring the ocean and the life it holds. Have students explore some of the qualities of ocean water with the experiments on this page. This first one will show whether it is easier to float in ocean water or freshwater. For every student group, you will need the following items: one egg; one jar filled with freshwater; one jar filled with ocean water. (To make your own ocean water, mix 2 teaspoons/ 10 mL of salt with 2 cups/480 mL of water.)

   Procedure: Place the egg in the jar of freshwater and observe what happens. (The egg sinks.) Next, place the egg in the jar of ocean water and observe what happens. (The egg floats in the jar.)

2. **Water Wonders.** Discuss the experiment results in activity 1. Ask students why they think objects float more easily in saltwater (oceans) than in freshwater. Let them see for themselves with the following experiment.

   Materials: two same-size clear glasses of water; ⅓ cup (80 mL) of salt; a spoon; a plastic straw; scissors; non-drying molding clay; colored thread

   Procedure

   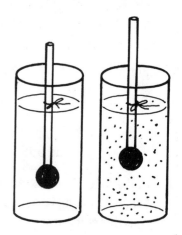

   - Place both glasses on a flat surface. Add all of the salt to one of the glasses and stir.

   - With the scissors, cut the straw so it is a little shorter than the glasses.

   - Roll the clay into a ball about the size of a marble. Stick the clay ball on the end of the straw. Tightly seal the connection between the straw and the clay to prevent water seepage into the straw.

   - With the clay end down, float the straw in the freshwater. (You may have to remove or add clay to get the straw to balance.)

   - Remove the straw from the glass and tie a piece of thread around the middle of the straw. Return it to the freshwater glass. Adjust the thread by sliding it up or down on the straw so that it marks the water level. This straw device is a hydrometer, an instrument for measuring the specific gravity of liquids.

   - Remove the hydrometer from the freshwater and place it in the saltwater. Adjust the thread to the new water level. (Saltwater is more dense than freshwater so objects float in it more easily.)

Teacher Reference_____

Cousteau, Jacques. *The Living Sea*. N. Lyons Books, 1988.

_____ *The Silent World*. N. Lyons Books, 1987.

Oceans. Teacher Created Materials, #284.

Student Reading

Carvel, Blair. *Exploring the Sea*. Random House, 1986.

Cole, Joanna. *The Magic School Bus on the Ocean Floor*. Scholastic, 1992.

Greene, Carol. *Jacques Cousteau: Man of the Oceans*. Children's Press, 1990.

Marine Life

When Jacques Cousteau explored the underwater world, he found many amazing fish and plants that had never been seen before. See how many of these underwater creatures you can identify. Read the descriptions below and write the creatures' names in the boxes provided. Use the Ocean Life Box to help you.

1
Its waving tentacles make it look like a plant, but it is actually an animal.

2
This sea animal resembles a plant.

3
This snakelike sea creature is also electric.

4
It has five arms and hundreds of tube feet to help it move.

5
This animal stings with its deadly tentacles.

6
At about 100 feet (30 m) long, it is one of the largest sea creatures.

7
This animal doesn't have its own shell; it must borrow one.

8
This plant is often a home for sea otters.

9
This sea mollusk can squirt an inky fluid to protect itself.

Ocean Life Box

jellyfish	coral	starfish
anemone	eel	kelp
squid	hermit crab	blue whale

Charles Darwin

Naturalist _____

Charles Darwin was born on the same day as Abraham Lincoln — February 12, 1809 — 4,000 miles across the sea in Shrewsbury, England. His parents were well-to-do and prosperous. Charles' father expected him to follow in his footsteps and become a doctor, but this was not to be. Although Charles did graduate from Cambridge University with a degree in divinity, his real interest was in studying nature. He was able to obtain a non-salaried position as a naturalist on a five-year cruise around the world. During that time he studied plant and animal species and collected fossils. Some species were collected and brought back to England with him for further studies.

While Darwin was in the Galapagos Islands, he noticed that there were many variations among the tortoises and among the finches. Upon his return to England, he studied the finches. He found that these variations or differences were what helped some animals to survive. In one case, for example, he observed that round-billed finches who lived on the ground were able to survive by gathering nuts and grains. Pointed-billed finches, however, were used to living in the trees. On the ground they were not able to gather food easily and eventually died out.

From these and other observations, Darwin formulated his theory of evolution through natural selection. His theory implies that when a particular variation in a plant or an animal enables it to survive more easily in a particular environment, the variations will be continued through future generations. His first book on the topic, *Origin of Species*, was printed in 1859 and sparked a storm of controversy. Although he never received any honors for his work, Darwin's theories about evolution changed the thinking of scientists, philosophers, writers, and politicians forever.

Suggested Activities

1. **Indispensible Thumbs.** Humans have evolved opposable thumbs. The human thumb can swivel at its base and can touch the tip of each finger. Only a few animals, such as chimpanzees, have opposable thumbs.

   To experience just how useful thumbs are, have the students tape their thumbs to their palms. Then let them perform any of the following tasks: drink from a glass; write with a pencil; pick up a tennis ball; or open a door. Afterwards, discuss the importance of thumbs.

2. **Stereoscopic Vision.** Humans have the ability to judge distances and focus on objects. This is called stereoscopic vision. Give students the chance to view the world through one eye with the following activity. Divide the class into groups of two. Give each pair a bean bag or ball to toss and an eye patch.

   - One partner tosses the ball to the other partner ten times. Record how many times the ball was caught.

   - The same partner tosses the ball ten more times while the other partner wears an eye patch. Record the number of catches.

   - Have the partners change roles and follow the same procedures. Compare the results of each ball toss variation. In which situation did the students experience greater success in catching the ball?

3. **Making a Fossil.** To help students understand how fossils are formed, have them make a print of a sea shell. Each child will need a clean, small milk carton, some sea shells, petroleum jelly, and plaster of Paris.

   - Coat the shells with petroleum jelly. Place them in the bottom of the milk carton. (You may want to grease the inside of the milk carton.)

   - Cover the shells with a layer of plaster of Paris and allow the plaster to dry.

   - Remove the milk carton and break open the plaster.

Teacher Reference

Berger, Melvin. *Famous Men of Modern Biology*. Thomas Y. Crowell, 1968.

Meadows, Jack. *The Great Scientists*. Oxford University Press, 1987.

Student Reading

Burton, Virginia Lee. *Life Story*. Houghton Mifflin, 1963.

Cole, Joanna. *The Human Body: How We Evolved*. William Morrow & Company, 1989.

Kaney, Regina. *The Glow in the Dark Book of Animal Skeletons*. Random House, 1992.

Powell, Whitney. *Traces of Life*. Morrow Junior Books, 1989.

Quackenbush, Robert. *The Beagle and Mr. Flycatcher: A Story of Charles Darwin*. Prentice, 1983.

Stein, Sara. *The Evolution Book*. Workman Publishing, 1986.

Ward, Peter. *The Adventures of Charles Darwin: A Story of the Beagle Voyage*. Cambridge University Press, 1982.

The Brain

The human brain is the one feature that truly sets people apart from other animals. Our brains are three or four times larger than most mammals of our size.

Different areas of the brain control various bodily functions such as breathing, thirst, and heartbeat. Unscramble the letter groups to find the names of the different brain parts. Use the Word Box to help you.

Word Box

medulla	cerebellum	pons
spinal cord	midbrain	cerebrum

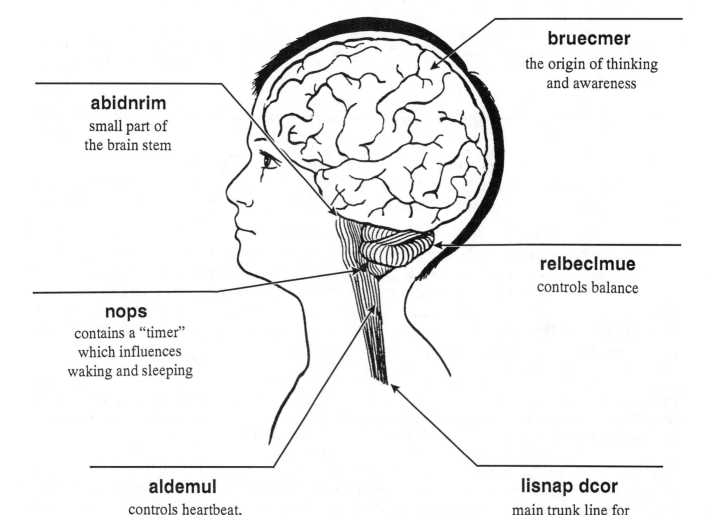

abidnrim

small part of
the brain stem

bruecmer

the origin of thinking
and awareness

nops

contains a "timer"
which influences
waking and sleeping

relbeclmue

controls balance

aldemul

controls heartbeat,
blood flow, breathing

lisnap dcor

main trunk line for
nerve pathways to
and from the brain

Galileo Galilei

Astronomer and Physicist

In his 78-year life span, Galileo Galilei — commonly known as Galileo — revolutionized the world of science. Although many of his ideas were original, he did borrow some from the Middle Ages and the ancient Greek Period.

Galileo's life began on February 15, 1564, just two months before Shakespeare was born. His father, Vincenzio, was a professional musician. Vincenzio wanted his son to become a doctor, but Galileo left the University of Pisa after four years to study mathematics on his own.

For a while he taught at the University of Padua and tutored students for extra money. Some of these students wanted to learn math for military engineering or for navigation. Galileo developed a geometric military compass for them.

In addition, Galileo discovered the laws of falling bodies. This law states that all falling bodies are governed by the same laws regardless of size. That is, an object will fall a certain distance in a certain amount of time, whether it weighs one pound (450 g) or one ton (828 kg). It is believed that Galileo conducted an experiment to prove his theory by dropping weights from Pisa's Leaning Tower. During this same time period, Galileo formulated the basis of ballistics; its principles are used in gunnery and rocketry. Finally, he discovered the law of how a pendulum works.

At the age of 46, Galileo began working with the telescope. He was one of the earliest observers of sunspots (dark areas on the sun's surface due to somewhat lower temperature in these areas). With the telescope, he was able to view phases on the planet Venus, to identify four moons of Jupiter, and to observe mountains on the moon.

Galileo continued experimenting, even after he became blind in 1637. Because of his beliefs that the earth revolved around the sun, he was at odds with the Roman Catholic Church, which made him retract those findings. It wasn't until October of 1992, that the Church settled the long-time feud, three and one-half centuries after Galileo's death on January 8, 1642.

Suggested Activities

1. **Playground Pendulum.** A playground swing is a familiar example of a pendulum. Visit a play area and have students draw pictures of a playground swing at rest and in motion. Observe the swing in motion when no one is in the seat and compare it to the swinging action when someone is sitting in the seat. Brainstorm with students a list of other examples of pendulums they have seen.

2. **Triangular and Square Numbers.** Galileo loved math and was able to use triangular and square numbers to explain the theory of falling bodies. Have student pairs or groups make triangular and square numbers. Supply each group with counters (dry cereal or beans, plastic coins, buttons, etc.). Direct students to make the following patterns and then build the next two in each series.

Triangle: (1) ● (2) ●●● (3) ●●●●●● (4) ●●●●●●●●●●

Square: (1) ● (2) ●●●● (3) ●●●●●●●●● (4) ●●●●●●●●●●●●●●●●

Have the students explain the relationship between succeeding triangles/squares.

(The difference between the number of dots in succeeding triangles: 2, 3, 4, 5, 6, 7...)

(The difference between the number of dots in succeeding squares: 3, 5, 7, 9, 11, 13...)

3. **A Riddle.** Read *Five Secrets in a Box* by Catherine Brighton (E.P. Dutton, 1987). Encourage students to discover the significance of each of the five objects in the box and how it relates to Galileo's life and experiments.

4. **Moon Talk.** Galileo discovered that there were mountains, valleys, and craters on the moon. To expand students' knowledge of the moon, pose the following questions. Have students work in research groups to discover the answers.

   - What are the phases of the moon?
   - Do other planets have moons?
   - How does the moon affect the tides?
   - Can life as we know it exist on the moon?

Teacher References_____

Meadows, Jack. *The Great Scientists*. Oxford University Press, 1987.
Silverburg, Robert. *Four Men Who Changed the Universe*. G.P. Putnam's Sons, 1968.

Student Reading

Branley, Franklyn. *Gravity Is a Mystery*. Harper Collins, 1970, 1986.
Brighton, Catherine. *Five Secrets in a Box*. E.P. Dutton, 1987.
Lauber, Patricia. *How We Learned the Earth Is Round*. Harper Trophy, 1990.

Galileo's World

Scientists today know much more about our galaxy than did the scientists in Galileo's time. During the years Galileo lived (1564-1642), it was a widely held belief that the earth was stationary, while the sun and planets orbited around it. Galileo's studies showed that the earth and other planets orbit around the sun.

With the help of the newly-invented telescope, Galileo discovered sunspots, the phases of Venus, and four moons of Jupiter. Think of what he might have discovered given today's modern equipment and technology! Even with high-powered telescopes it took scientists until 1930 to discover Pluto, our outermost planet.

The chart below contains some information about the nine planets. Write the name of the planet in the space provided.

Name of Planet	Symbol	Facts About the Planet
1.	☿	This planet is closest to the sun and moves the fastest.
2.	♀	It is the brightest planet.
3.	⊕	This is the only planet known to be inhabited.
4.	♂	This reddish-colored planet is Earth's neighbor.
5.	♃	It is the largest planet.
6.	♄	This planet has rings around it.
7.	♅	Discovered in 1781, it can barely be seen.
8.	♆	This planet was named after the god of the sea.
9.	♇	The last to be discovered, it is the farthest planet from the sun.

Matthew Henson

Explorer _____

Some critics question whether Admiral Peary and Matthew Henson ever reached the North Pole in April 1909. They doubted that Peary's observations were accurate and they dismissed Henson as an uneducated African-American. Although the truth may never be known, it is unlikely that Admiral Peary could have journeyed so far without the help of Matthew Alexander Henson.

Henson was born on a Maryland farm, in 1865, just one year after the Civil War had ended. When he was two years old, his mother died. Nine years later his father died. To escape his cruel stepmother, Matt ran away to Washington, D.C., to live with his uncle. For a while, Matt worked as a dishwasher. Then he signed on as a cabin boy on a ship bound for Hong Kong. Under the Captain's guidance, young Matt learned to read and write. In addition, he learned seamanship, navigation, math, geography, and first-aid. During his five years of travel, Henson learned about many cultures and could speak several different languages.

On his return to the states, Henson worked at a clothing store. One day Robert Peary went into the store to buy a tropical sun helmet. Matthew Henson was called on to help Peary. During the course of their conversation, Peary asked Henson to accompany him on his journeys as his servant. Henson accepted the appointment. Within a short time, Matthew Henson was promoted to field assistant to the survey crew.

Henson accompanied Peary on six expeditions in search of the North Pole. On their second journey, the team discovered three meteorites which are now on display at the American Museum of Natural History in New York. Henson and Peary measured and recorded temperatures which sometimes reached 29 degrees below zero Fahrenheit (-34°C). They also mapped the terrain and took photographs. Despite sub-freezing Arctic conditions, the expedition reached the North Pole on their sixth expedition. That famous date is April 6, 1909. On that same date in 1988, 33 years after his death, Matthew Henson was reburied in Arlington National Cemetery next to Admiral Peary.

Suggested Activities

1. **Magnetic North.** One of the instruments used by Peary's crew included the compass. Students can build their own compass with just a few common items. **KIT**

   Materials: one large darning or sewing needle; a ½" (1.3 cm) thick slice of cork; small saucer of water; magnet; masking tape

   Procedure: Magnetize the needle by sliding one end of the magnet 20 times along the length of the needle, in the same direction. Tape the needle to the flat side of the cork. Place the cork in the saucer filled with water. Observe the needle as it settles into a north-south pattern.

   Alternative Activity: Provide each group of students with the materials listed. Challenge them to make a compass using only these materials.

2. **Meteorites.** Matthew Henson and Admiral Peary returned from their second expedition with two meteorites. Ask students to define meteorite, meteoroid, and meteor. Establish the correct definitions. Have students create a chart to show the difference between the three terms. Research some meteorites, such as the one found near Grootfontein, South Africa, or the well-known Barringer.

3. **Make an Island.** Greenland is the world's largest island. Have students build their own island with sand, rocks, and water. Pour a layer of sand to cover the bottom of a shallow dish. Arrange the rock on the sand and add water until the rock is about one-fourth covered. Add other features to the island. Ask each student to name his/her island and attach an index card describing its location, flora and fauna, and topography.

4. **Salt Water Freeze.** On his expeditions to the North Pole, Matthew Henson encountered bitter-cold temperatures, ice, and snow, in addition to the salty waters of the Arctic Ocean. Expose students to properties of water in the presence of salt with the following activity. You will need a bowl of water, a match, some salt, and an ice cube.

   Procedure: Place the ice cube in the bowl of water. Lay a match on top of the ice cube. Sprinkle some salt around the match and observe what happens. (The match will become frozen into the cube. This happens because salt water freezes at a lower temperature than ordinary water. The salt water that forms around the match does not freeze as quickly as the plain water under the match. The underside of the match becomes frozen into the ice. You can then use the match to lift the ice cube out of the water.)

Teacher References_____

Adams, Russell L. *Great Negroes: Past and Present.* Afro-Am Publishing Company, 3rd rev.ed., 1984.

Grant, Neil. *A Salute to Black Pioneers.* Empak, 1986.

Student Reading

Ferris, Jeri. *Arctic Explorer: The Story of Matthew Henson.* Carolrhoda Books, 1989.

Gilman, Michael. *Matthew Henson.* Chelsea House, 1988.

Comparing Temperatures

Scientists use a number of temperature scales in their specialized fields. Two of the most common ones are the Fahrenheit (abbreviated F) and the Celsius (abbreviated C) scales. The Fahrenheit thermometer measures the freezing point of water at 32°F; the boiling point of water is 212°F. On the Celsius thermometer, the freezing point is 0°C and the boiling point of water is 100°C. Use the diagram below to answer the following questions.

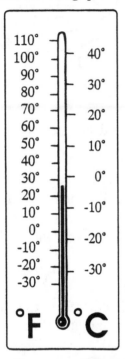

1. If it is 30° C outside, is it hot or cold? _____

2. When the temperature is -30°C, about what temperature is it on the Fahrenheit scale? _____

   _____

3. If an outdoor thermometer has a reading of 40° and it is very hot outside, which temperature scale is being used?

   _____

4. When it is -10° (10° below 0) below 0 on the Celsius scale, about what temperature is it on the Fahrenheit scale?

   _____

5. The Fahrenheit thermometer reads 40°. Is that hot or cold?

   _____

Calculator Challenge

You can calculate the temperature from one scale to the other by using the following equations:

- To find the Celsius temperature when the Fahrenheit temperature is known, subtract 32 degrees from the Fahrenheit temperature, then multiply that number by .55.

$$(°F - 32) \times .55 = °C$$

- To find the Fahrenheit temperature when the Celsius temperature is known, multiply the Celsius temperature by 1.8 and add 32 to the product.

$$(°C \times 1.8) + 32 = °F$$

Use the equations above to calculate the following temperatures. (Round to the nearest degree.)

(A) 65° F = _____ ° C   (D) 85° F = _____ ° C

(B) 40° C = _____ ° F   (E) 100° F = _____ ° C

(C) 5° C = _____ ° F   (F) 200° C = _____ ° F

Maria Mitchell

Astronomer

In 1986, a young woman working at Palomar Observatory near San Diego, California, discovered a comet. But it did not bring her the fame and glory that befell Maria Mitchell some 139 years earlier. After all, Maria's discovery had been made without the use of the sophisticated techniques and equipment available today.

Maria's life began in 1818 on Nantucket Island in Massachusetts. Her father was a dedicated astronomer and teacher. He was also a Quaker and believed that girls deserved the same education as boys. This was at a time when it was generally considered unimportant for girls to get any education. By the time Maria was four years old she could read. At night she learned to read the stars. When she was 12 years old, she helped her father record the timing of a solar eclipse.

As a young woman, Maria worked as a librarian and continued her rooftop observations. Fortunately, the bank where her father worked had built a new observatory complete with a four-inch (10 cm) telescope. Then, on October 3, 1847, she discovered a comet and asked her father to confirm her findings. Over the course of a few days, she continued to observe the comet. Mr. Mitchell wrote to Professor Boyd, an astronomer at Vassar College in Poughkeepsie, New York. The professor, in turn, wrote of the discovery and sent a letter to the King of Denmark. A gold medal had been offered by the King to the first person finding a comet by using a telescope. After some dispute, Maria Mitchell was declared the winner.

This sudden fame opened up various opportunities for Maria. She was asked to work on a nautical almanac, which included information about tides, phases of the moon, and eclipses. In 1875, she was appointed President of the Women's Congress' third annual meeting. Maria also traveled extensively and even saw — but could not use — the Vatican's telescope in Rome. America's first woman astronomer died in 1889, in Lynn, Massachusetts.

Suggested Activities

1. **Model an Eclipse.** When Maria Mitchell was 12 years old, she observed a solar eclipse. This occurs when the moon passes directly in front of the sun. Have students model a solar eclipse. You will need a lamp, an old tennis ball, and a pencil.

   Procedure: Push the pencil into the tennis ball; this represents the moon. Turn on the lamp and turn off all the other lights. (This demonstration works best in a darkened room.) Stand 10 to 15 feet (3m - 4.5 m) from the lamp and table. Hold up the moon at arm's length. Keep one eye closed as you move the moon in orbit around the earth until the moon (ball) covers the sun (lamp) to produce an eclipse.

   For more information on modeling an eclipse see *Astronomy Activity Book* by Dennis Schatz (Simon & Schuster, 1991) or *Eclipse: Darkness in Daytime* by Franklyn Branley (Harper Trophy, 1973, 1988).

2. **Indoor Planetarium.** Have each student choose a different constellation (for more common constellations and their configurations see *The Stargazer's Guide to the Galaxy* by Q.L. Pearce, RGA Publishing Group, 1991). Each student will also need an empty cereal box, a pencil, and a flashlight. **KIT**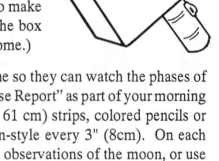

   Procedure: With the pencil, draw an X to mark the position of each star in the constellation. Then use the pencil to punch holes in the X's to make the pattern. In a darkened room, shine the flashlight up through the box and onto the ceiling. (You may want students to try these out at home.)

3. **Moon Phases.** Students can make a moon phases chart to take home so they can watch the phases of the moon each night. Make a classroom chart. Include a "Moon Phase Report" as part of your morning activities. Distribute white butcher paper cut in 3" x 24" (8 cm x 61 cm) strips, colored pencils or marking pens, and rulers. Have students fold the paper accordion-style every 3" (8cm). On each square, draw and label a different phase of the moon. Make visual observations of the moon, or use moon phase information from the newspaper. Compare it to the chart. (Charts may be taken home for continued use.)

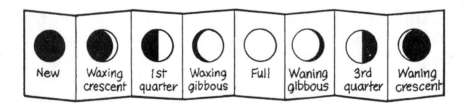

Teacher References_____

Bennett, Wayne, ed. *Women Who Dared To Be Different*. Garrard, 1973.

Gilford, Henry. *Heroines of America*. Fleet, 1970.

Merriam, Eve. *Growing Up Female in America*. Beacon, 1987.

Student Reading

Baker, Rachel. *America's First Woman Astronomer, Maria Mitchell*. Julian Messner, 1960.

McPherson, Stephanie Sammartino. *Rooftop Astronomer: A Story About Maria Mitchell*. Carolrhoda, 1990.

Celestial Visions

Maria Mitchell became an astronomy teacher in 1865, at Vassar College in Poughkeepsie, New York. She taught her female students by sharing her work with them and by allowing students to assist her in the observatory.

Read the paragraphs below to discover some of the celestial sights they observed. Then draw the missing parts in each picture.

1. To view the total eclipse from Denver in 1877, Maria and her students had to wear protective dark glasses. The moon almost covered the sun, leaving a bright halo surrounding the moon's black disk. Color the disk black. Color the halo yellow.

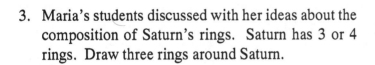

2. The students watched Maria take photographs of sunspots which are huge, dark, "cooler" areas on the sun. Draw and color two sunspots on the sun.

3. Maria's students discussed with her ideas about the composition of Saturn's rings. Saturn has 3 or 4 rings. Draw three rings around Saturn.

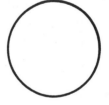

4. The students listened attentively as Maria told them her theories about Jupiter. They watched the moons travel across the face of the planet. Jupiter has 16 known moons. Draw some moons around Jupiter.

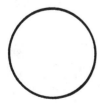

5. Maria would call to her students to watch an unexpected meteor shower, even if it was late at night. A meteor is a chunk of rock or dust plunging to the earth. As it heats up, it leaves behind a glowing streak of light. Draw a meteor in the space provided.

John Muir

Conservationist

When John Muir's family moved from Scotland to America in 1849, he was only 11 years old. Even at that young age, he was able to appreciate the beauty of the woods on their Wisconsin farm. At 22, he went to a state university despite his father's disapproval. After college, John worked in a carriage manufacturing company. An accident left him temporarily blinded. During his recovery, he thought about all the beautiful things he might never see again. It was at this point in his life that John Muir decided to become a naturalist.

Muir began a one-thousand mile walk to Florida. Along the way, he studied trees and flowers in detail. He traveled unarmed because he did not believe in killing animals. A blanket, some flour, and tea were all he carried in his pack. He wore his clothes in layers rather than carry a bulky coat. Above all, he appreciated nature for its beauty.

When John heard about the wonders of Yosemite, he went to see it for himself. His first visit lasted only 10 days, but he took a job as a shepherd and then worked in a saw mill to have money to return. At the saw mill, he refused to cut down live trees. He continued to explore Yosemite. Muir even found living glaciers at work, thus proving his theory that Yosemite Valley had been created by glaciers. Previously it had been thought that it was formed by earthquakes.

With the building of the transcontinental railroad beginning in 1864, and the influx of homesteaders, the environment was threatened. John began to write articles to warn of the shrinking wilderness. He also wrote articles about the beauty of Yosemite and the necessity of making it a national park. Due to his efforts, Yosemite National Park with an area of 1,100 squares miles, was created in 1890.

John Muir, often called the father of our national parks, continued to lobby for the preservation of national lands, especially the Grand Canyon and Arizona's Petrified Forest.

Suggested Activities

1. **Magnify It.** On his expeditions, John Muir used a barometer, a watch, and a magnifying glass to help with his observations. Directions for a homemade barometer appear on page 36.

   In this lesson, students can make a simple magnifying glass.

   Materials: fast-food take-home bucket or cardboard ice cream bucket; plastic wrap; rubber band (large enough to fit around the top of the bucket); water; a variety of small objects (seeds, grass, flowers, etc.); knife

   Directions: With the knife, cut a hole in one side of the bucket as shown. Stretch the plastic wrap across the top of the bucket. Secure the plastic wrap in place with the rubber band. Pour some water (¼ cup/60 mL) onto the plastic wrap. Through the side hole, place an object on the floor of the bucket. Observe it through the water. Have students view several objects through this simple magnifier. Ask them to sketch their observations and share them with the class.

   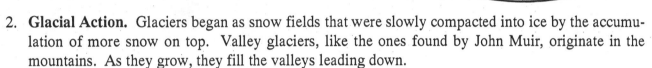

2. **Glacial Action.** Glaciers began as snow fields that were slowly compacted into ice by the accumulation of more snow on top. Valley glaciers, like the ones found by John Muir, originate in the mountains. As they grow, they fill the valleys leading down.

   Valley glaciers are great movers of materials on the earth's surface. They gouge out large depressions and carry along soil and other debris to be deposited elsewhere. Simulate glacial action with this demonstration.

   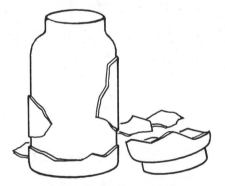

   Materials: glass jar with lid; water; a freezer; paper bag

   Directions: Completely fill the glass jar with water. Place the jar in the paper bag before putting it in the freezer. Observe what happened by the following day. Establish that the freezing water broke the jar much as water breaks rocks when it seeps into cracks and then expands when it freezes. Caution students not touch the broken glass. Dispose of materials carefully.

Teacher References

Allison, Linda. *The Sierra Club Summer Book.* Sierra Club Books, 1977.
Katz, Adrienne. *Naturewatch.* Addison-Wesley, 1986.
Mc Cormick, Maxine. *Sequoias and Kings Canyon.* Crestwood, 1988.

Student Reading

Bender, Lionel. *Glaciers.* Franklin Watts, 1989.
Force, Eden. *John Muir.* Silver Burdett, 1990.
Greene, Carol. *John Muir: Man of the Wild Places.* Children's Press, 1991.
Krensky, Stephen. *Four Against the Odds.* Scholastic, 1992.
Naden, Corinne J. and Rose Blue. *John Muir: Saving the Wilderness.* The Millbrook Press, 1992.
Stewart, John. *Winds in the Woods: The Story of John Muir.* The Westminster Press, 1975.

National Parks

You will need library resources such as reference books for this activity. Read each description below. Then draw a line from it to the national park that is described.

1. The fossil remains in this Arizona park feature the largest display of petrified wood in the world.

2. This spectacular gorge was cut by the Colorado River in Arizona. It is up to one mile deep in some places.

3. Majestic peaks can be seen in this area of the Rocky Mountains in Wyoming. You will find Jackson Hole here, too.

4. Established in 1890, this California park features the highest falls in North America and the giant sequoias.

5. A swampy region in Florida, this area was inhabited by the Seminoles. In 1947, it was made a national park.

6. Kilauea and Mauna Lea are active within this island park. At both, people can hike up to see the lava flow.

7. Some 300,000 bats can be found in these caves. Limestone "rooms" are filled with stalactites, stalagmites, and crystals.

8. Here the salty tides of the Atlantic Ocean and the rocky granite coastline meet. Evergreen and maple forests lie above.

Hawaii Volcanoes
National Park

Acadia
National Park

Carlsbad Caverns
National Park

Grand Canyon
National Park

Yosemite
National Park

Petrified Forest
National Park

Grand Teton
National Park

Everglades
National Park

Joanne Simpson

Meteorologist

After Pearl Harbor was attacked in 1941 and the United States had engaged in war with Japan, the American people were eager to help with the war effort. Even the students at the University of Chicago, where Joanne Simpson was attending classes, were volunteering their help. The Army, Navy, and Air Force were in desperate need of meteorologists. Updated information on the weather conditions was crucial to the flying and landing of planes. Due to the shortage of men, many women, including Joanne Simpson, were chosen by the military for instructor positions, to help in the training of military personnel.

Once the war ended, Joanne applied for meteorologist positions but was turned down because she was a woman. In graduate school, she encountered more prejudice from men who tried to discourage her from a career in meteorology. Joanne Simpson secured a position at the University of Chicago, where she met and married an assistant professor of meteorology. Subsequently, she was fired from her job because at that time both husband and wife could not be employed by the same school. Since she was a woman, she, and not her husband, had to leave.

Despite these obstacles, Joanne continued to pursue her career goals. In 1960, she was made full professor of meteorology at UCLA. This time she was allowed to stay on the faculty, even though her new husband worked in the same department.

Joanne Simpson is best known for her pioneering research in cloud-seeding. She also conducted experimental work in hurricane modification. (This involves the dispersion of silver iodide smoke-filled flares above the cumulus storm clouds, causing hurricanes to lose some of their force.) For her work, Ms. Simpson was awarded the Gold Medal Award from the United States Department of Commerce.

Her dedication to the pursuit of her goals has made Joanne Simpson an admired heroine to women around the world.

Suggested Activities

1. **Make It Rain.** Demonstrate how rain forms with this activity. You will need a hot plate, 2 bricks, a metal ice cube tray, a large metal cookie sheet, ice cubes, a tea kettle, and water.

   Procedure: (For safety, always provide adult supervision when a heating element is involved.) Fill the tea kettle with water, place it on the hot plate, and turn on the hot plate. Place the cookie sheet next to the kettle and hot plate as shown. While the water is coming to a boil, place the bricks on opposite ends of the cookie sheet, just close enough to balance the ice cube tray (filled with ice cubes) on the two bricks. When the tea kettle boils, aim the spout directly under the metal ice tray. The steam from the kettle will cause condensation to form on the bottom of the tray, and soon it will begin to "rain."

2. **Build a Barometer.** Meteorologists use a variety of instruments in their work. One of them is the barometer, which is a gauge to measure air pressure. Group the students and supply each group with the following items: one balloon; one rubber band; a 3" x 5" (8 cm x 13 cm) index card; scissors; a marking pen; a large jar (such as a mayonnaise jar); a plastic straw; tape. Challenge the students to build a device to measure the air pressure.

   Solution: Cut off the neck of the balloon and discard it. Stretch the remaining balloon surface across the mouth of the jar. Secure it with a rubber band. Tape the straw on the balloon "lid" as shown. Place the jar on a flat surface next to a wall. Tape the index card to the wall so that the level of the straw falls somewhere in the middle of the card. Write HIGH on the card above the level of the straw. Write LOW on the card below the level of the straw. Add numbers as shown in the illustration. Observe the position of the straw over several days. Record the barometric pressure and discuss the results. (When the air pressure is high, air will push down on the balloon's surface causing the straw to indicate high. The reverse occurs under low pressure conditions.)

3. **Rain Gauge.** Measure the amount of rainfall with this device. You will need a wide-mouthed jar, a funnel, a foam meat-packing tray, scissors, and a shovel. Bury the jar in the ground so that its mouth is at ground level. Make a hole in the tray and fit the spout into the hole. Place the plastic onto the mouth of the jar. Measure the amount of rainfall in the jar after a rainfall. **KIT**

Teacher References_____

Noble, Iris. *Contemporary Women Scientists in America.* Julian Messner, 1979.
Weather. Teacher Created Materials, #273.

Student Reading

Branley, Franklyn. *Flash, Crash, Rumble and Roll.* Harper & Row, 1985.
Cosgrove, Brian. *Weather.* Alfred A. Knopf, 1991. (An Eyewitness Book)
The Weather Tracker's Kit. Running Press (available at large book stores)

Cloud Formations

Meteorologists learn to read cloud formations to help them predict upcoming weather. The clouds pictured below represent some of the earth's cloud formations. See how well you can identify them. Read the definitions noting the cloud name for each. Then write the cloud name on or near the matching cloud. Use reference books to help you.

Cumulus: Dense, billowy clouds heaped upon one another. (1,600 - 20,000 ft./480 m - 6 km)

Cirrostratus: Form ice crystals that veil the sky with a milky look. (over 20,000 ft./6 km)

Stratocumulus: Large, rounded masses with light and dark areas. (ground to 6,500 ft./ground to 2 km)

Altocumulus: Have various shapes; may form bands across the sky. (6,000 - 20,000 ft./1.8 - 6 km)

Stratus: Low, smooth layer of clouds; resembles fog. (ground to 6,500 ft./ground to 2 km)

Cirrus: Wispy clouds that look like tufts of hair. (sometimes higher than 30,000 ft./9 km)

Alexander von Humboldt

Biogeographer

Some say that Alexander von Humboldt was second in fame only to Napoleon during his lifetime. It is a well-deserved honor because he made a number of significant contributions in a variety of scientific fields.

Alexander was born in Berlin, in 1767, in what was then known as Prussia. He and his brother studied privately under a tutor before going on to the University of Göttingen. There, Alexander met a naturalist and together they explored all of Europe. The voyage made him eager to travel to South America, but he realized he would need more relevant science studies.

In 1791, he entered the Academy of Mines where he met Abraham Werner, an important figure in the history of geology. Werner provided the first widely accepted rock classification system.

During his 5-year tour of South America, von Humboldt obtained plant specimens and collected data, much of which was unknown to European scientists. These observations led to the new science of biogeography, which determines the distribution of living things on the Earth's surface. Based on his data and observations, von Humboldt wrote a 5-volume book titled *Kosmos*, the first respectable encyclopedia of geography and geology.

Von Humboldt's other main accomplishments concern magnetism. He noticed that compass needles sometimes began to oscillate backwards and forwards in "magnetic storms." His research suggested that the Earth's magnetism was affected by activity on the sun (a theory explored today by man-made satellites). Von Humboldt also noticed that some rocks had a magnetism of their own.

In addition, Alexander von Humboldt produced maps of Mexico and the Louisiana Territory, instituted a successful search for diamonds in the Ural Mountains, and was a pioneer ecologist. Von Humboldt, who died in 1859, contributed greatly to science, particularly in that he influenced others to look at things in a different way.

Suggested Activities

1. **Ecological Maps.** Divide the class into small groups. Assign each group of students a different biome (tundra, forest, desert, rainforest, grassland, ocean). Direct them to research that biome and to locate the various animals that inhabit each location. Discuss why a rainforest animal could not live in the ocean, or why a tundra inhabitant could not survive in the desert. Distribute "A Biome Chart" (page 40) to each group. As a class, discuss the results of each group's research. Have students add information to complete their charts.

2. **Cut-Aways.** Give each student a sheet of white construction paper and a pair of scissors. Have students fold the paper in half and cut out a circle leaving part of the fold uncut. With colored pencils or pens students can draw, color, and label the earth's crust, mantle, outer core, and inner core on the top circle. On the inside page, tell students to define the terms *igneous*, *sedimentary*, and *metamorphic*. You may want them to list the names of some rocks that are examples of each family.

3. **Floating Rocks.** Bring in a variety of rocks, including pumice, for students to examine. Ask them to predict what will happen to each rock as you place it in a jar of water. Why does the pumice float? (It is a type of lava that contains gas bubbles which make it light enough to float. It is the only rock light enough to float.)

4. **Rock Hunt.** Take the students on a walking field trip to gather rock samples, or assign the students to find rocks as homework. Pair the students so they can identify and classify the rocks. Have them glue a sample to a sheet of construction paper, write its name below the rock, and name its rock family. Display all the rocks at a special center or table in the classroom.

As an extension, ask each student to choose one rock from his or her collection to be a "pet rock." Have students use the form on page 41 to experiment with and to learn more about their "pet rocks." (Materials needed for this activity include a rock, a ruler, a scale, a nail, a penny, vinegar, and a container of water.)

Teacher References_____

Baker, J.N.L. *A History of Geographical Discovery and Exploration.* Cooper Square, 1967.
Franck, Irene M. and David M. Brownstone. *Scientists and Technologists.* Facts on File, 1988.
Rocks and Soil. Teacher Created Materials, #265.

Student Reading
Bresler, Lynn. *The Usborne Book of Earth Facts.* Usborne Publishing, Ltd, 1986.
Gaines, Anne. *Alexander von Humboldt: Colossus of Exploration.* Chelsea House, 1991.
Gans, Roma. *Rock Collecting.* Harper & Row, 1984.

A Biome Chart

A biome is made up of a geographical region and the plants and animals that inhabit it. Climate largely determines which plants and animals thrive in a specific environment. Each kind of animal is suited only to a certain climate. An Arctic hare, for example, would not survive long in a tropical forest. There are six main types of biomes — Arctic tundra and ice, forest, desert, rain forest, grassland, and ocean. In general, these biomes follow the pattern of the climate zones. (See insert below.)

Fill in the chart below with the names of ten animals that live in the biome section to which you have been assigned. Research other biomes and write a few animals' names in each one. Add other students' contributions to your chart as well.

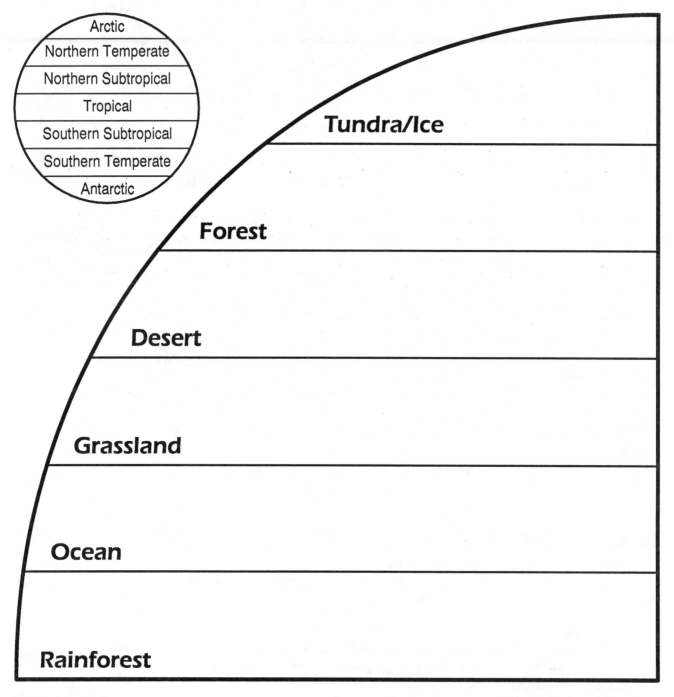

"Pet Rock" Experiment

Draw a picture of your "pet rock" in the box to the right.

Where did you find your rock?

_____

Describe your "pet rock."

_____

_____

_____

_____

Now conduct your experiment. Predict what you think the answers will be and write them down in the chart below. After the experiment, write down the results. Compare your findings with other students' results.

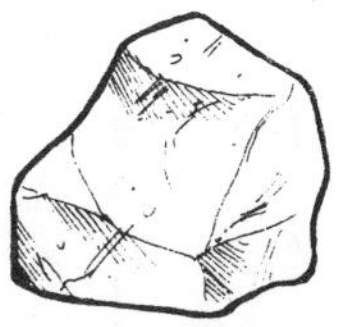	**Length** Measure with a ruler.	**Weight** Weigh on a scale.	**Hardness** Which will scratch your rock?*	**Acid** Does your rock bubble when vinegar is dropped on it?**	**Floats** Does your rock float or sink?***
Prediction					
Results					

	Hardness Number	
*Hardness scale: A fingernail can scratch rock.	2	A soft rock
A penny can scratch rock.	3	↕
A nail can scratch rock.	4	A hard rock

** If there are bubbles appearing on your rock, it has lime (or calcium carbonate) in it. This mineral is found in limestone and marble.

*** Rocks that float usually have come out of a volcano. Was the area where you live ever a volcano?

Life Scientists

Below is a listing of the life scientists who are represented in this section. Following each name is a brief summary of related information.

Scientist	Area of Study	Country of Origin	Achievement
Rachel Carson (1907–1964)	Environmental Studies	U.S.A.	brought public attention to dangers of DDT
George Washington Carver (1864–1943)	Chemurgy	U.S.A.	found over 300 commercial uses for the peanut
Eugenie Clark (1922–)	Marine Biology	U.S.A.	studied sharks; discovered natural shark repellant
Sigmund Freud (1856–1939)	Psychoanalysis	Austria	considered father of psychoanalysis; used hypnotherapy
Jane Goodall (1934–)	Ethology	England	pioneered primate studies; discovered that chimps make tools
Percy L. Julian (1899–1975)	Chemistry Research	U.S.A.	developed a synthetic cortisone from soybeans
Barbara McClintock (1902–1992)	Genetics	U.S.A.	experimented with maize; discoverer of "jumping genes"
Margaret Mead (1901–1978)	Anthropology	U.S.A.	studied cultures and developed the science of anthropology
Gregor Mendel (1731–1806)	Botany	Austria	experimented with pea plants; founded basic laws of heredity
Louis Pasteur (1822–1895)	Bacteriology	France	developed pasteurization and vaccines for anthrax and rabies
Daniel Hale Williams (1856–1931)	Medicine — Surgery	U.S.A.	became first doctor to perform surgery on the heart
Rosalyn Yalow (1921–)	Medical Research	U.S.A.	developed the radioimmunoassay method

Rachel Carson

Environmentalist

Rachel Louise Carson was born on May 27, 1907, in Springdale, Pennsylvania, a small rural village north of Pittsburgh. Her mother, Maria, was her closest companion and she nurtured in Rachel a love of the outdoors and nature. Maria also encouraged her daughter not to accept less in life just because she was a woman.

Rachel attended Pennsylvania College for Women (now known as Chatham College) on a four-year tuition scholarship. English was her major as she wanted to be a writer. After taking a course in biology, Rachel switched majors to zoology to write about animals and make them come alive to others.

When she tested for a position as junior aquatic biologist, she surpassed all the other applicants. The Bureau of Fisheries (now the Fish and Wildlife Services) hired Rachel to write stories for their radio program. She also began writing about the ocean; her first book was *Under the Sea Wind*. Next came *The Sea Around Us* in 1951; it remained on the New York Times best-seller list for 86 weeks.

After receiving a letter from a friend, Ms. Carson began to investigate the effects of DDT, a powerful synthetic insecticide. Her friends told of the deaths of robins after DDT had been sprayed over their yards. From her research emerged *Silent Spring*, which warned against the dangers of pesticides.

Many honors were bestowed upon Rachel Carson including the Audubon Medal (the first time it was ever given to a woman) and the Cullum Medal of the American Geographical Society. A most prestigious honor was bestowed upon her when Rachel Carson was elected to the American Academy of Arts and Letters.

Suggested Activities

1. **Outdoor Observations.** Take the class on an outdoor field trip to quietly observe things in nature. Or assign for homework 15 to 30 minutes of quiet observation times at a nearby woods, pond, seashore, etc. Have students draw pictures of the plants, flowers, insects, and animals observed. Tell the students to identify them or do research to find out more about the things they observed. Encourage students to ask questions about the surroundings, for example, "Do bees like buttercups better than roses?" Discuss the steps necessary to solve such a problem. If feasible, conduct an actual experiment.

2. **DDT.** DDT is an abbreviation for dichlordiphenyl trichloroethane, a powerful synthetic insecticide used to kill a variety of insects, including lice, flies, and mosquitoes. Unfortunately, it also killed and poisoned birds and wildlife. Pesticides seeped into water systems and contaminated drinking supplies. Thanks to Rachel Carson, the United States restricted the use of DDT beginning in 1972.

    For homework, have the students make a list of all the pesticides in their homes. Read the dangers written on the containers. What are the effects if ingested? What are the antidotes? What are some alternative methods of pest control? Discuss possibilities as a class. Then, prepare the following alternative methods of discouraging ant infestations.

    Homemade Ant Repellent: Students can make their own ant repellent by mixing equal parts of borax and powdered sugar. Sprinkle the mixture in infested areas. To keep ants from infesting gardens, plant marigold, tansy, chives, and lavender among the plants.

3. **"Write" a Wrong.** Start this activity by conducting a whole-class brainstorming session on things that are ecologically wasteful. These can include conditions that students have experienced, such as leaky faucets, or have heard about, such as oil spills. Record each idea on a separate piece of paper and place each in a fish bowl or other container. Each day students are to draw one topic from the bowl and write ways that the problem can be solved. Have students share their solutions in small groups. Each group then chooses one problem and prepares a set of solutions to be shared in a large group session.

Teacher References_____

Carson, Rachel. *Silent Spring*. Houghton Mifflin, 1962.
_____ *The Sea Around Us*. Oxford University Press, 1950 .
Ecology. Teacher Created Materials, #286.
Jezer, Marty. *Rachel Carson*. Chelsea House, 1988.
Our Environment. Teacher Created Materials, #272.

Student Reading

Goodman, Billy. *How To Save the Planet*. Avon Books, 1990.
Harlan, Judith. *Sounding the Alarm: A Biography of Rachel Carson*. Dillon Press, Inc., 1988.
Henricksson, John. *Rachel Carson*. The Millbrook Press, 1991.
Kudlinski, Kathleen V. *Rachel Carson: Pioneer of Ecology*. Puffin Books, 1988.
Wadsworth, Ginger. *Rachel Carson: Voice for the Earth*. Lerner Publications, 1992.

Beauty in Nature

Rachel Carson loved writing about the sea and about the beauty she found in nature. In a letter to a friend she once said, "I will try in my writing to make animals in the woods or waters, where they live, as alive to others as they are to me."[1]

Choose a favorite ocean or land animal. In the space below, make that animal come alive by drawing a picture and describing it in words.

[1]Bonta, Marcia Myers. *Women in the Field*. Texas A & M University Press, 1991.

George Washington Carver

Chemurgist

George Washington Carver never knew his parents. His mother was abducted by slave raiders when he was an infant and his father died shortly before in a farming accident. For most of his youth, George was raised by a white couple, the Carvers, in Diamond Grove, Missouri. When he was 12, he set out on his own to find a school that would allow blacks to attend. His travels took him to Missouri, Iowa, and Kansas. George earned money by working as a farmhand, cook, and laundry helper.

In 1894, George graduated with honors from Iowa State College. He was offered a post there as director of the greenhouse. During this time, he discovered a new kind of fungus plant that grows on the leaves of red and silver maple trees. Carver's work in agriculture was becoming widely known.

When Tuskegee Institute opened its doors for black students, George Washington Carver was asked to head the Department of Agriculture. Not only would he be involved in research, but he would also be responsible for helping and teaching the farmers. For years they had been planting cotton; now the soil lacked nutrients. To make matters worse, the boll weevil infested and destroyed acres of cotton. Carver told them to plant goobers, more commonly known as peanuts. That season produced an overabundance of peanuts and no one knew what to do with them. George went to work in his lab and began analyzing the peanut. He found that he could extract a substance similar to cow's milk and was able to make cheese from it. After mashing peanuts, he was able to use the oil to make cooking oil, soap, and body oil. Peanut shells could be used to make soil conditioner and insulating board. Altogether, he discovered over 300 products that could be created from peanuts.

After his death on January 5, 1943, George Washington Carver was buried on the campus of Tuskegee Institute. Five years later, the United States honored him with a three-cent postage stamp which included his picture.

Suggested Activities

1. **Make Peanut Butter.** Students can work together in pairs to prepare homemade peanut butter. Start with roasted, unsalted peanuts. Have students shell and hull the peanuts. (Save the peanut shells for use with activity #2.) Put 1 cup (about 250 mL) of peanuts in a blender. Add 2 tablespoons (30 mL) of vegetable oil and ¼ teaspoon (1 mL) of salt. Grind until smooth. Have your class taste their creation on crackers or apple slices while brainstorming other uses of peanuts.

2. **Peanut Puppets.** Using the peanut shells from the previous activity, have students choose shell pieces that fit over their fingers. Direct them to draw faces on the shells with a fine-line marking pen. Groups of students can write, direct, and present their own original plays about an event(s) in the life of George Washington Carver.

3. **Fry-Off.** You will need two electric fry tubs or skillets, sweet or russet potatoes, peanut oil, and a vegetable oil. Pour peanut oil into the fry tub and vegetable oil into the other; heat as directed. Cut the potatoes into chunks and fry some in each type of oil. Drain the cooked potatoes on paper towels and allow to cool.

    Blindfold a student and ask him/her to taste a potato from each batch. Could he/she tell which kind of oil each potato chunk was cooked in? Record the results along with which one they preferred. Allow a number of students to take part in the potato tasting. After all the results have been recorded, have students make summary statements (e.g., Three out of five students couldn't taste the difference between potatoes cooked in peanut oil and potatoes cooked in vegetable oil.).

4. **Story Sequence.** Read *A Pocketful of Goobers* by Barbara Mitchell (Carolrhoda Books, 1986) to the class. Ask students to take notes highlighting important events, people, and places in the life of George Washington Carver. From their notes, have each student write one fact on a 3" x 5" (8 cm x 13 cm) index card. Have groups of four or five students arrange cards in story sequence. Ask one member of each group to read the cards in sequence while you complete a story map on the board.

Teacher References _____

Cobb, Vicki. *Science Experiments You Can Eat.* Harper & Row, 1972

Plants. Teacher Created Materials, #224.

Student Reading

Adair, Gene. *George Washington Carver.* Chelsea House, 1989.

Benitez, Maria. *George Washington Carver, Plant Doctor.* Raintree Publication, 1989.

Hayden, Robert C. *Seven Black American Scientists.* Addison-Wesley, 1970.

Peanut Products

By the time George Washington Carver died in 1943, he had found over 300 uses for the common peanut. Listed below are just a few of his discoveries. You will have to unscramble the letter groups to learn what they are. Use the Peanut Box to help you.

1. turbet   _ _ _ _ _ _

2. asop   _ _ _ _

3. kni   _ _ _

4. leacre   _ _ _ _ _ _

5. lsctipas   _ _ _ _ _ _ _ _

6. eaprp   _ _ _ _ _

7. acbleh   _ _ _ _ _ _

8. lmki   _ _ _ _

9. eysd   _ _ _ _

10. dncya   _ _ _ _ _

11. tmea ucsae   _ _ _ _   _ _ _ _ _

12. edrdi focfee   _ _ _ _ _   _ _ _ _ _ _

Peanut Box

plastics	dried coffee	candy
bleach	meat sauce	ink
dyes	milk	soap
butter	cereal	paper

Eugenie Clark

Marine Biologist_____

On Saturdays, Eugenie's mother would sell newspapers at a downtown newspaper stand in New York City. The extra money was sorely needed, since Eugenie's father had died when she was a baby. While her mother worked, Eugenie would spend her time at the local aquarium. It was there that her love of fish began. In addition to fish, Eugenie collected toads, salamanders, and snakes. When she joined the Queens County Aquarium Society, she became its youngest member.

After graduating from Hunter College in New York, Eugenie went to work for Carl Hubbs, a famous California ichthyologist (scientist who studies fish). When her studies with him were complete she worked at the Museum of Natural History in New York and attended classes at New York University. Next she was asked to go to the South Sea Islands to learn about poisonous fish. By this time, Eugenie had won many scholarships to study fish.

After she was married, Eugenie and her husband opened a marine lab in Florida where she set out to learn all she could about sharks. Special pens were built in the water to facilitate observations. While they lived in Florida, Eugenie and her husband had four children.

When the marriage ended, Eugenie and her children moved to Maryland where she taught at the University. Summers were spent on the Red Sea where Eugenie Clark first observed a fish, called the Moses sole, that sharks would not and could not eat. Further investigations of the Moses sole showed that it emits a poison which paralyzes sharks and acts as a natural repellent.

Dr. Eugenie Clark, who was born in 1922, still studies the underwater world.

Suggested Activities

1. **Measure It.** A nurse shark was one of the guests in the new pens at Eugenie Clark's marine laboratory in Florida. Nurse sharks can grow to 14-feet (4 meters) in length. To represent a nurse shark, tape a fourteen foot (4 meter) length of masking tape to the classroom floor (or draw a 14-foot/4 meter chalkline on a sidewalk). Have the students predict how many students, lined up back-to-back, it would take to equal the 14-foot length. Direct them to line up on the tape.

2. **Tricky Niki.** On one of her diving expeditions to the Red Sea, Eugenie found a new species of fish. She named the fish Trichonotus nikii after her son. The word Trichonotus refers to the long rays of the fish's fan. Tricky Niki is its common name while Trichonotus nikii is its scientific name. Find out the scientific names of some common fish. Pair the students and have them make a chart of common and scientific names of at least ten fish.

    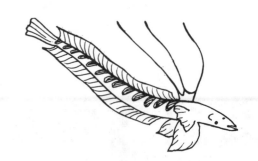

3. **Inside a Shark.** Dissect an actual shark. Small sharks may be available from fresh fish markets or fishing piers. An adult may have to demonstrate a dissection for the class. If a shark is not readily available use a smaller, more common fish. For help with dissecting procedures, see David Webster's *Dissection Projects* (Franklin Watts, 1988).

    Follow-Up Activity: Tell the students to draw the outline of a shark on a sheet of drawing paper. Direct them to draw and label the brain, mouth, throat, heart, liver, rib, intestine, kidney, esophagus, vertebral column etc.

4. **Mural.** Read *The Desert Beneath the Sea* by Ann McGovern and Eugenie Clark (Scholastic, 1991). On a long strip of butcher paper, have the class draw and color a mural of the desert beneath the sea. Label all the fish with their common and scientific names.

5. **Aquariums.** Keep a classroom aquarium. Rotate the feeding and care of the fish among the students. Have students keep a daily log of observations of the fish over a period of time.

    Visit a local aquarium. Have the students identify as many forms of sea life as they can. After returning to the classroom, make a class list of all the fish observed. Classify them by feeding habits, habitat, size, etc.

Teacher References_____

Clark, Eugenie. *The Lady and the Sharks.* Harper & Row, 1969.
_____ *Lady With a Spear.* Harper & Row, 1953.
Emberlin, Diane. *Contributions of Women: Science.* Dillon Press, 1977.
Oceans. Teacher Created Materials, #284.

Student Reading

Cole, Joanna. *Hungry, Hungry Sharks.* Random House, 1986.
_____ *The Magic School Bus on the Ocean Floor.* Scholastic, 1992.
Mc Govern, Ann. *Shark Lady: The True Adventures of Eugenie Clark.* Macmillan, 1978.
Mc Govern, Ann and Eugenie Clark. *The Desert Beneath the Sea.* Scholastic, 1991.

Name That Shark

Read the description above each shark pictured on this page. Write the correct shark name in the space provided. Use the names in the Shark Box to help you.

1 This tiny shark is no bigger than your hand.

_____ shark

2 The largest of the sharks has 3,000 teeth.

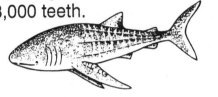

_____ shark

3 These "wolves of the sea" stay together in packs.

_____ shark

4 This strange-looking shark has a tool-like head.

_____ shark

5 This shark is easy to spot. It is about 4 feet (1.2m) long.

_____ shark

6 This small fish lies on the ocean floor like a rug.

_____ shark

7 This shark gets its name from its stripes.

_____ shark

8 This dangerous shark is named for its white belly.

_____ shark

Shark Box

tiger	great white	carpet	blue
whale	hammerhead	dwarf	leopard

Sigmund Freud

Psychoanalyst _____

Thanks to Sigmund Freud we now know that our emotions play a very important role in our mental health. His explorations of the mind left scientists a legacy of ideas to study and to challenge.

Freud was born on May 6, 1856, in Freiburg, Germany. His father was a poor, Jewish wool merchant who lavished attention on Sigmund and instilled in him a love of learning.

Sigmund began his career as a research zoologist in the field of neurology (the study of the nervous system). In 1882, he joined the staff of the Vienna General Hospital where he continued his work tracing nerve tracts in human brains. He also studied hypnotism and used the method to cure patients of hysteria (mental illnesses). Under hypnosis, a subject freely talked about problems which were buried in the subconscious mind, thus clearing the person's mind of painful memories. Another method employed by Freud was "free association." Using this method, a patient said whatever came to mind and was able to talk about what was too frightening to even think about.

Freud believed that dreams allowed people to think about problems or situations which in the waking state are buried in the subconscious. He wrote books on both dream analysis and on the causes of mental illness. When Adolf Hitler came to power in 1933, he had all of Freud's books burned. Freud himself moved to London where he continued his work. The "father of psychoanalysis" died on September 23, 1939.

Suggested Activities

1. **Research.** Assign small groups of students to research any of the following topics; have them present their findings to the class.

   • Explain why Hitler ordered the public burning of all of Freud's books.

   • Define hypnotism. Explain how it works and tell how it is used for medical purposes. (For more information read *Hypnosis: The Wakeful Sleep* by Larry Kettelkamp, Human Science Press, Inc., 1971).

   • Phrenology claimed that the brain could be mapped into 35 distinct regions. Each of these regions controlled a different characteristic of human behavior (love of food, intelligence, etc.). Compare a diagram of a brain according to phrenologists with the current maps of neural anatomy. Draw and label a picture of each.

2. **Neurons and Behavior.** The body contains over 99,980 miles (161,000 km) of nerves in the nervous system. Each nerve is composed of cells called neurons. These neurons carry nerve impulses or messages from one neuron to another. For example, sensory neurons carry messages from our eyes, nose, ears, skin, and tongue to the central nervous system. Freud studied neuropathy (diseases of the nervous system) by tracing nerve tracts in brains. The information and experiments below will help students understand this topic better.

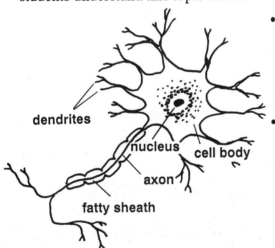

dendrites

nucleus

cell body

axon

fatty sheath

   • Reflex actions occur when something causes you to react without thinking about it. Sit on a chair and cross your legs so that one leg swings freely. With the side of your hand, gently but firmly hit the soft area below the kneecap of the free leg. Discuss what happens.

   • Divide the class into pairs of students. Give one partner in each pair a cotton ball and the other a sheet of clear plastic to hold up in front of his/her face. The other partner tosses the cotton ball at the plastic sheet. What reflex action occurs? On the next toss, try to keep from blinking. Have the partners exchange roles.

3. **Feelings.** Discuss feelings with the class. A good way to introduce the topic is to read a selection from Aliki's book, *Feelings* (Greenwillow Books, 1984). For example, read aloud to students the page that talks about conscience. Afterwards discuss the meaning and the purpose of a conscience.

Teacher References _____

Hollischer, Walter. *Sigmund Freud: An Introduction.* Ayer Company Publishers, 1947.

Meadows, Jack. *The Great Scientists.* Oxford University Press, 1987.

Russel, Peter. *The Brain Book.* Hawthorn, 1979.

Student Reading

Aliki. *Feelings.* Greenwillow Books, 1984.

Baker, Rachel. *Sigmund Freud.* Julian Messner, 1952.

Emotions

Emotions are strong feelings we experience. Love, joy, pride, and sorrow are just a few of the emotions that we have. People react differently to different emotions based on past experiences and learned behavior.

Each box below lists a different emotion. In each box, write about or draw a picture of an incident that caused you to experience that emotion. Tell how you reacted. You may want to discuss some of these emotions with a partner.

Frustration	**Happiness**

Anger	**Loneliness**

54

Jane Goodall

Ethologist

During World War II, Jane Goodall's family moved to the safety of a house in the English countryside. It was on the neighboring farm that Jane began her first observations of animal behavior. She wanted to learn how chickens lay eggs so she crouched inside a henhouse to find the answer. Another incident that shaped her future, she claims, is the Christmas she received the book, *The Story of Dr. Doolittle*. After reading the story, she knew she wanted to go to Africa to observe wild animals.

In 1957, her wish come true. Jane had saved enough money to visit a friend there. The friend, in turn, introduced Jane to Dr. Leaky, an anthropologist and paleontologist. Jane worked as an assistant until 1960 when she went to Gambe in Tanzania, Africa, to study chimpanzees. At first, Jane had to search for the chimps who were very shy. It was a full year before any chimpanzee would approach within 100 yards.

As Jane observed the chimps, she collected samples of what they ate and recorded notes about their behavior. No one had studied wild chimpanzees before. Jane recorded notes about their behavior. Jane found that the animals traveled in groups of six or more and that they liked to eat bugs, figs, bits of meat, and bananas. One startling discovery was that the chimps could make and use crude tools. For example, one chimpanzee broke a twig off and placed it in a termite hole. When he brought it out of the hole, it was loaded with termites, which he proceeded to have for lunch!

In 1975, Jane established the Gambe Stream Research Center for Wildlife Research. She is well-known for her *National Geographic* films about chimpanzee life. Also, she has written three books including the best-seller, *In the Shadow of Man*.

Jane Goodall, born in London, England, on April 3, 1934, fought tirelessly for the humane treatment of chimpanzees.

Suggested Activities

1. **Africa.** Tell students to locate Africa on a globe. Have them find Gombe in Tanzania. Direct them to use a piece of string to measure the distance from Gambe to Jane Goodall's childhood home in London. Use the key on the globe to figure out how many miles Jane traveled to study the chimpanzees.

2. **Comparison.** Assign the students to read *My Life With the Chimpanzees* by Jane Goodall (Pocket Books, 1988) and *Diane Fossey* by Leah Jerome (Bantam Skylark Books, 1991). Have the students compare Jane's work with chimpanzees to Diane's work with gorillas.

SUBJECT: *Sparrow*			
DAY + DATE	FOOD	ACTIVITIES	OTHER BEHAVIORS
Tues, Jan. 5	worm	digging in ground for worm	flew to nest - chirped

3. **Record It.** Observe an animal in nature over a period of two weeks. Make a chart to record observations of what it ate, its activities, and other behaviors. If possible, collect samples of its food, any examples of tools used, or draw sketches of the daily observations. Have students share their findings with the class.

   Alternative: Students can make daily observations and drawings of a classroom pet (bird, hamster, rabbit, fish, etc.) if it is not convenient or possible for students to conduct such a study outside the classroom.

4. **About Chimps.** Divide the class into student pairs or small groups. Assign them to research information about chimpanzees. (*National Geographic* and *World* magazines are two excellent resources. Check with your librarian to find out what is available.) Direct groups to write a list of at least ten things they learned about chimpanzees. As a class, construct a chart to show the likenesses and differences between chimps and humans.

5. **Help Them.** Some chimpanzees and gorillas are endangered species. Tell the students to find out what they can do to help endangered species. An excellent source of information on this topic can be found in the book, *Earth Book for Kids: Activities To Help the Environment* by Linda Schwartz (The Learning Works, Inc., 1991). As a class, vote on a project they can do to help support endangered species.

Teacher References _____

Goodall, Jane. *In the Shadow of Man.* Houghton Mifflin, 1971.
Jungle. Teacher Created Materials, #283.

Student Reading

Birnbaum, Bette. *Jane Goodall and the Wild Chimpanzees.* Raintree Publishers, 1989.
Goodall, Jane. *Chimps.* Atheneum, 1989.
Lofting, Hugh. *The Voyages of Dr. Doolittle.* Delacorte Press, 1988.
Lucas, Andre. *Monkeys, Apes, and Other Primates.* Marboro Books, 1989.
Lucas, Eileen. *Jane Goodall: Friend of the Chimps.* Millbrook Press, 1992.

Chimpanzees or Gorillas?

You may have to do some research to find out which descriptions below apply to chimpanzees only, gorillas only, or both. Write the letter of each descriptive phrase from the box below in the proper section of the Venn diagram.

Descriptive Phrases

a. live in Africa   f. seldom attack   k. are the largest of the apes

b. are mammals   g. travel in small groups   l. sleep in a nest of branches

c. use simple tools   h. are primates   m. live in rain forests

d. live up to 50 years   i. throw things at enemies   n. male leaders called silverbacks

e. travel on the ground   j. are playful, curious   o. sometimes eat meat

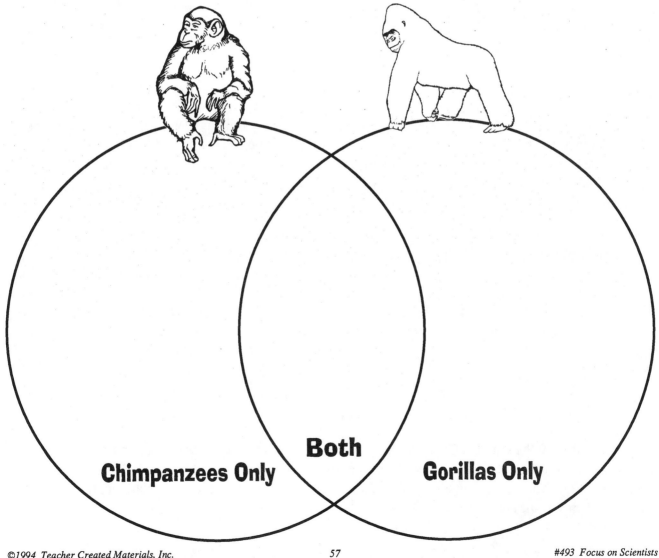

Chimpanzees Only   **Both**   **Gorillas Only**

Percy L. Julian

Research Chemist

Most people are aware of George Washington Carver's research on peanuts and their many uses. Fewer people know about the accomplishments of Percy Lavon Julian, an African-American research chemist who developed a number of important products from soybeans.

Percy was born on April 11, 1899 in Montgomery, Alabama, to a railway clerk and his wife. He was the oldest of six children. Since his high school had no advanced courses, Julian entered Depauw University in Greencastle, Indiana, as a "sub-freshman." He had to make up the many classes that he missed in high school. To help with tuition, he waited on tables at a white fraternity house and slept in the attic. Despite these hardships, he graduated with top honors and delivered the valedictorian speech.

After graduation, he accepted a teaching position at Fisk University where he won the Austin Fellowship. This allowed him to obtain a master's degree in chemistry from Harvard. Next, he went to Europe to study with Ernst Spaeth. Spaeth had been able to synthesize, or make artificially, several natural chemicals. When Julian returned to the United States, he began work on synthesizing a drug to treat glaucoma, a serious eye disease. The Glidden Company took notice of his work and hired him to develop a synthetic casein (a substance which makes paints waterproof). Julian began to study soybeans as a possible substitute and was able to extract a soybean protein that was similar enough to casein to be used.

The discovery of several very important soybean products followed. During World War II, Julian developed fire-fighting foam which was widely used to extinguish fires on U.S. Navy ships and crash-landed airplanes. Julian learned how to make a synthetic cortisone, which is used to treat arthritis, allergies, and asthma.

In 1953, Julian left the Glidden Company to build his own research company — Julian Laboratories — to learn how to extract sterols from yams. For his work, Julian was awarded the 1947 Spingarn Medal, the NAACP's highest honor, and was the first African American to be inducted in the National Inventor's Hall of Fame. Percy L. Julian died April 19, 1975.

Suggested Activities

1. **Legumes.** Like peas and beans, soybeans are legumes (plants which have seeds that grow in pods). Examine some dry peas, lentils, lima beans, or soybeans. Have students grow their own plants using the method outlined below. **KIT**

   Materials: styrofoam egg carton; soil; legumes; craft stick; water

   Directions: Cut the lid from the egg carton; place the top half on the lid. Fill each egg cup with soil. With the craft stick, poke a hole in the soil of each cup. Place a legume in each hole; cover it with soil. Sprinkle it with water and place it where it will get sun. Draw and/or write daily observations.

2. **Similarities.** Both Percy L. Julian and George Washington Carver discovered many uses from simple seeds. Julian worked with soybeans while Carver worked with peanuts.

   Have students read books about both men (see the Student Reading suggestions below and on pages 47.) Compare their childhoods, schooling, and accomplishments in a chart or Venn diagram.

3. **Useful Soybeans.** Many foods are made with soybeans. The list includes soybean milk, tofu, soy sauce, and soy flour. In addition, soybeans are used in some meat products at fast food restaurants, as ingredients in ice cream and frozen yogurt, and as meat substitutes.

   Visit a market where natural/organic foods are sold and find out about other food products that contain soybeans. If possible, make a dish containing tofu or soybeans. Many fine recipes can be found in *Recipes From a Small Planet* by Ellen Buchman Ewald (Ballantine Books, 1973).

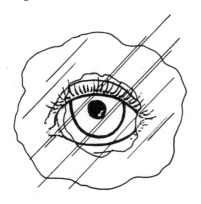

4. **Glaucoma.** Research glaucoma to find out its effects on eyesight. Let students simulate the effect of glaucoma on their eyes with this project. Cut a piece of clear plastic wrap to fit well over the eye. With petroleum jelly trace a thick circle on the plastic wrap to resemble the eye's circumference, leaving just a small eye-hole clear in the center. Tell students to hold the plastic up to one eye (make sure the petroleum jelly faces away from the eye). They should be able to see straight ahead, but not peripherally, thus mimicking the effects of glaucoma.

Teacher References

Green, Richard L. *A Salute to Black Scientists and Inventors.* Empak, 1985.
Haber, Louis. *Black Pioneers of Science and Inventions.* Harcourt, Brace, and World, 1970.

Student Reading

Hayden, Robert C. *Seven Black American Scientists.* Addison-Wesley, 1970.
Lee, George L. *Black American History Makers.* Ballantine Books, 1989.
Shalit, Nathan. *Cup and Saucer Chemistry.* Dover Publications, Inc., 1972.
VanCleave, Janice. *Chemistry for Every Kid.* John Wiley & Sons, 1989.
Yount, Lisa. *Black Scientists.* Facts on File, 1991.

All-Purpose Soybeans

Percy L. Julian believed that there were many uses for soybeans. Much of his research centered on finding out these various uses.

In the Product Box below, is a list of twenty things that can be manufactured from soybeans. Find and circle these products in the word search puzzle. Words may appear across, down, backwards, or diagonally.

Product Box

cooking oil	cosmetics	fertilizer	soap	flour
milk	whipped cream	mayonnaise	plastics	ink
margarine	shaving cream	paper coating	disinfectants	cortisone
cheese	candy	cattle feed	shoe polish	foam

```
M K P D M A B I O M A S B L O U H E X Q L M Y A
L N O I G N H N E D M Y F M G A F J I X S U D K
E B S E C O O K I N G O I L I O P M N G T M N B
X A T M U K N E D S I O M K A S J O P A U L A E
I M N V M R X M L M S Z M M L M E L C M O X C O
P R A M G N I T A O C R E P A P M H M S A Y S N
S W T N S H A V I N G C R E A M E O M S P A C M
C E C L M F R M Z A M C T S M E A J H O B L U H
I N E O H M M I N K Z M Z M S Q D L U V K I B N
T Y F P R W R L V T R X M E C H A L H O N E I E
E O N M T B A K E E M S H O E P O L I S H O M Y
M H I I M O H M Z N R C D E L N M U S Z I M H N
S E S G A R D I B O I M C N A K E A K J N L G M
O E I U G M L B E L L Y M I E N S T U C V G C S
C O D T M I I Y U F G D Q R M V I R S N I K R O
A M R W T M Y Y M L U Y O A B E A S U R K T Z A
E N O R E D N I W O R P M G H R N P M O R W M P
L T E M E M I H C P A L M R O E N O Z M L H E O
M F M S R C M I K N Q M H A T K O M S L M F P M
Q E C A T T L E F E E D M M D M Y V N I A L M I
L S X S D Q O K E Z N M W M O K A Y M D T M W P
K E D W D M B A N I L A O F G M M B M F X R M V
A N M B I S K I T M A E R C D E P P I H W M O M
H E E A U C M N R M Z O N D H I A C O R N C Q C
I M E D C M O Y F Y V M P L A S T I C S M R W D
```

Barbara McClintock

Geticist

In 1951, Barbara McClintock read her research paper describing her six years of lab work to a group of scientists. It was met with silence. The audience did not understand what they had heard and some even considered the ideas bizarre. Undeterred, Barbara retreated to her lab to continue her experiments.

Barbara McClintock was born on June 16, 1902, in Hartford, Connecticut. She was considered a tomboy in her youth. She asked for a set of tools when she was six years old and was the only girl on her block's baseball team. Her parents objected to her going to college because they were afraid no man would want to marry her. Barbara prevailed, however, and she attended Cornell University in Ithaca, New York, where she majored in botany (the study of plants). While working toward her doctorate she turned to plant genetics (the study of inherited traits in plants).

McClintock studied the function of each of the ten pairs of maize (corn) chromosomes and the effects of X-rays on the genetic makeup of corn. She later discovered that everyone was wrong about genes and chromosomes. Gregor Mendel had previously demonstrated that inherited characteristics were logical and predictable, but McClintock found that genes could "jump," indulge in random behavior, and could even pass from cell to cell.

Once Barbara McClintock's theories were accepted by the scientific community, it was possible for her to study antibiotic-resistant bacteria, seek a cure for African sleeping sickness, and study how cancers work in the body.

In 1983, Barbara McClintock was awarded the Nobel Prize for Medicine and Physiology. She was also granted an honorary doctorate from Harvard University in 1979 and won the first McArthur Laureate Award which provided her with an annual income of $60,000 for life.

For over 50 years, McClintock worked tirelessly, without the help of lab assistants, in her maize patch. She was content with her quiet lifestyle and died peacefully in 1992.

Suggested Activities

1. **Close-Up Exam.** Slice a thin section from an ear of corn. Rub ink over the surface of one side. View the non-inked surface with a magnifying lens. Look at the pipes through which water and food once flowed through the cornstalk.

2. **Corn Is Maize:** Read *Corn Is Maize: The Gift of the Indians* by Aliki (Crowell, 1976) aloud to the students. Follow up with a corn product tasting party. Sample corn on the cob, corncakes, corn tortillas, etc. Or, make and eat popcorn. You may wish to string some popcorn to make jewelry or design pictures using popcorn seeds and/or popcorn flakes.

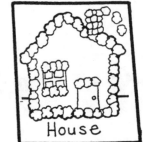

3. **Sprouting Plants.** Divide the class into groups of two for this activity. Each student pair will need a glass jar or clear plastic cup, blotting paper, popcorn kernels soaked in water overnight, and water. Direct the students to wet the blotting paper with water and line the inside of the jar with the wet paper. Place corn between the glass and the blotting paper. Students can easily observe the growth of the corn. Have them write about or illustrate daily observations.

4. **Genetic Information.** Establish some background information about genes and chromosomes. Every cell in our bodies is filled with pairs of microscopic threads called chromosomes. Along each chromosome are thousands of bead-like structures called genes. These genes contain chemical instructions that tell your body to make certain parts of you. For example, some genes carry directions for building the shape of your nose while other genes give directions about your ability to digest foods. Human cells contain 23 pairs of chromosomes, or 46 chromosomes altogether.

Assign students to do any of the following.

- Research what happens when an extra chromosome is present.
- Explain the difference between x and y chromosomes.
- Tell how cells divide. Draw and label the steps.
- Compare Barbara McClintock's work with corn to Gregor Mendel's work with pea plants.

Teacher References_____

Current Biography Yearbook. H.W. Wilson Company, 1984.
Kent, Charlotte. *Barbara McClintock.* Chelsea House, 1991.
Vare, Ethlie Ann and Greg Ptacek. *Mothers of Invention.* William Morrow and Company, 1988.

Student Reading

Bornstein, Sandy. *What Makes You What You Are.* Julian Messner, 1989.
Dash, Joan. *The Triumph of Discovery: Women Scientists.* Julian Messner, 1990.
Kittredge, Mary. *Barbara McClintock.* Chelsea House, 1988.

The Popcorn Plant

For over fifty years, Barbara McClintock worked with maize, commonly known as Indian corn.

Read the descriptions of the plant parts below. Use the information to label the corn plant with the correct names.

ear and husk: The ear is the seed-bearing spike of the corn plant. Each ear contains clusters (rows) of female flowers called silk. Surrounding the ear is the husk, a dry outer covering which protects the silk and kernels.

leaves: The leaves grow out from the nodes. Veins run lengthwise through the leaves which make the edges look wavy.

nodes: (joints) Nodes separate the stalk into sections. These joints help make the plant stronger.

prop roots: Prop roots are extra above-ground roots that help "prop up" tall corn plants.

silk: The female flower located in the ear is called the silk. Each strand of silk, when fertilized by the pollen, will form one corn kernel.

tassel: The tassel is the male flower located at the top of the plant. It sheds pollen which is "caught" by the silk.

roots: The roots are located below the ground part of the plant. They serve as an anchor and absorb water and nutrients.

stalk: The main stem of the corn plant is called the stalk. It supports the plant.

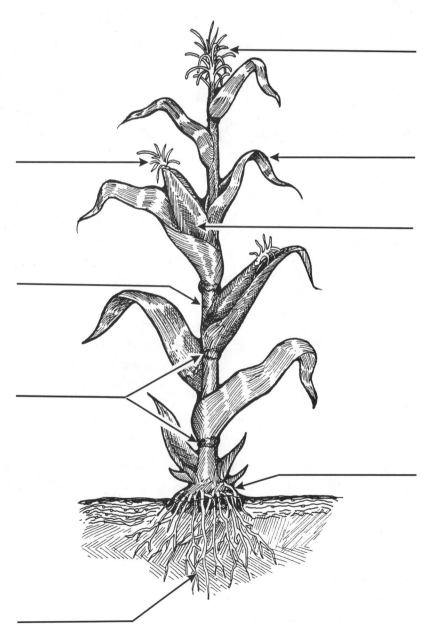

Margaret Mead

Anthropologist _____

Margaret Mead is credited with creating the science of anthropology, as she was the first scientist to extensively study the physical, cultural, and social lives of human beings. Her upbringing may have had something to do with her life's interest.

She was born December 16, 1901, in Philadelphia, Pennsylvania to a university professor and his sociologist wife. Professor Mead's job required extensive relocations, and by junior high school age, Margaret had lived in 60 different houses. She easily adapted to new and strange environments. She enjoyed watching people and wondered what made families so alike and yet so different.

Mead's higher education began at Barnard University where she studied sociology; she graduated in 1923. Two years later, she left for Samoa to study adolescent girls.

Margaret wanted to know if teenage problems were the results of hormonal and physical changes or were due to societal pressures. In her studies she concluded that the Samoan female adolescents experienced an easier transition to adulthood than did their American counterparts. Margaret Mead's first book, *Coming of Age in Samoa: A Psychological Study of Primitive Youth for Western Civilization* (William Morrow, 1928), was based upon her observations there. Next, she went to New Guinea to live with and study the Manus people. This time, Margaret studied pre-adolescents by having them draw pictures. She hoped the drawings would help her understand how they viewed the world. When Mead studied the Bali children, she developed the techniques of interviewing, observing, note-taking, and photographing that are still used today by anthropologists all over the world.

Suggested Activities

1. **Alike and Different.** With students, construct a Venn diagram to show how they are alike and different from children of another culture. Or, construct a chart comparing likenesses and differences between them and children of another period of history. Discuss some current problems students face: drugs, gangs, violence, AIDS. How are these problems alike or different from students of a different era or culture?

2. **Genealogy.** Assign students the task of finding out about their family heritage as far back as possible. Who is the oldest living member of the family? Who is the youngest? Direct the students to construct a family tree using index cards or self-stick notes. Have them print a different family member's name on each card. Arrange them into a tree pattern on a flat surface (a large sheet of posterboard, for example). Or, reproduce page 66 and have students work with family members to complete the family tree. For help in building a family tree, consult the book, *Do People Grow on Family Trees? Genealogy for Kids and Other Beginners* by Ira Wolfman (Workman, 1991).

3. **Case Study.** When Margaret Mead studied a culture, she used the techniques of note-taking, observing, interviewing, and photographing. Ask students to choose a family member to observe for a one or two week period. Have them prepare a list of questions to ask during an interview. For example, students might ask "What is the best thing about being the oldest child in this family?", "Do you enjoy it or not?", or "What do you dislike most about being the oldest?"

After conducting an interview, observe that person daily. Take notes describing actions made by that family member which have to do with any questions asked during the interview. If possible, take a picture of the interviewee working at a task or doing something related to questions in the interview. Make a construction paper cover for the report. Be sure to include any conclusions you may have been able to draw from your observations.

Extension: Keep records of the amount of time the subject spends on eating, studying, sleeping, and enjoying recreational activities. Make a graph to show how that person spends his or her time.

Teacher References

Emberlin, Diane. *Contributions of Women: Science.* Dillon Press, 1977.

Mead, Margaret. *Coming of Age in Samoa: A Psychological Study of Primitive Youth of Western Civilization.* William Morrow, 1928.

_____ *Family.* Macmillan, 1965.

Noble, Iris. *Contemporary Women Scientists of America.* Julian Messner, 1979.

Student Reading

Beller, Susan Provost. *Roots for Kids: A Genealogy Guide for Young People.* Betterway Publications, 1989.

Castiglia, Julie. *Margaret Mead.* Silver Burdett Press, Inc., 1989.

Epstein, Sam and Beryl. *She Never Looked Back.* Coward, McCann and Geoghegan, 1980.

Saunders, Susan. *Margaret Mead: The World Was Her Family.* Viking Kestrel, 1987.

A Family Tree

Fill in the spaces with the names of your family members. You may need help from a parent to gather the information needed to complete this tree. If you can provide the names of great-grandparents, etc., add them to the top of the tree, or on the back of this paper.

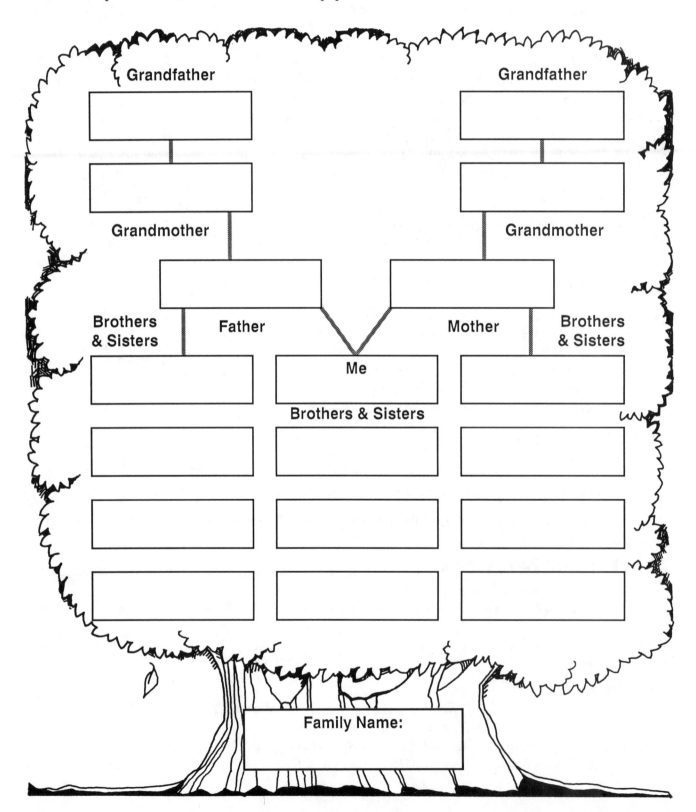

Grandfather

Grandfather

Grandmother

Grandmother

Brothers & Sisters

Father

Mother

Brothers & Sisters

Me

Brothers & Sisters

Family Name:

66

Gregor Mendel

Botanist

It is hard to imagine that an Augustinian monk of the 19th century would provide the basis for modern genetics. However, that is precisely what happened.

Born in 1822 in Heinzendorf near Austria, Gregor Mendel learned his love of gardening from his father who was a farmer. Gregor attended high school in a nearby town.

Since his family was so poor and could not afford to pay the full tuition, Gregor received only half the amount of food as the other boys. He nearly starved, and the experience remained in his memory forever.

On the advice of a professor he greatly admired, Gregor entered the monastery where he could continue his studies. There he became the caretaker of the gardens and a substitute teacher for an elementary school.

From 1856 until 1864, Mendel worked with 10,000 specimen pea plants. He cross-fertilized 22 kinds of peas and studied seven characteristics of the plants. After eight years of accurate record-keeping, he formulated three laws that became the basis of the science of heredity. He proudly wrote a paper to describe his findings. No one seemed to recognize the genius of his work, though, and Gregor was crushed. In 1883, he died of a heart attack, embittered that no one recognized or appreciated his scientific revelations.

Then, in 1990, three botanists from three different countries completed papers on the heredity of plants. Each of them had come across Mendel's paper when they made a routine check of the scientific literature before they published their own findings.

In each case, Mendel's forgotten paper reached the same conclusions that they had reached. Gregor Mendel's time had finally come.

Suggested Activities

1. **Dominance.** The first of Mendel's laws states that some inherited traits are dominant; others are recessive. Dominant means that one pair of genes masks another and prevents it from appearing. One dominant human trait is the ability to roll the edges of the tongue into a U-shape. Tell the students to try rolling their tongues in this way. Find out what percentage of the class has this dominant trait. (About 3 out of 10 students will be unable to roll their tongues in a U-shape.)

2. **Coin Toss.** Use coin tossing to help students better understand how inherited traits are determined. Coin tossing provides a mathematical example of the combinations that result from a predetermined set of circumstances. For example, examine two coins. If they are thrown into the air, there can be three results: Head-Head; Head-Tail; Tail-Tail.

HEAD-HEAD	HEAD-TAIL	TAIL-TAIL
‖‖ ‖‖ ‖	‖‖	‖‖ ‖‖
%	%	%

   Pair the students and direct them to construct a chart similar to the diagram at right. Have them toss two coins into the air and allow them to land freely on a flat surface.

   On the chart, tally the number of times each combination occurs. Repeat for a total of 50 tosses. Have student pairs calculate the percentage of each combination. Discuss the groups' results and relate the activity to the inheritance of traits in humans.

3. **Find Out Why.** Students will learn why people look alike or different when they read *Grandfather's Nose: Why We Look Alike or Different* by Dorothy Hinshaw Patent (Franklin Watts, 1989). Genes, chromosomes, and other topics are explained in easy-to-understand terms. Follow up with the activity on page 69.

4. **Punnett Squares.** These diagrams show how traits are combined when they pass from parent to offspring. If a pure short pea plant (represented by tt) for example, is crossed with a hybrid tall pea plant (represented by Tt), two offspring are hybrid tall (Tt) and two are pure short (tt). The resulting diagram will look like this:

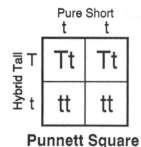

Punnett Square

   Begin by combining the T and t in the upper left corner; then, the T and t in the upper right corner; next, the t and t in the bottom left corner; and finally, the t and t in the lower right corner.

   Have students diagram a cross between a pure yellow corn (YY) and a hybrid yellow corn (Yy).

Teacher References_____

Berger, Melvin. *Famous Men of Modern Biology.* Thomas Y. Crowell, 1968.
Halacy, Jr., D.S. *They Gave Their Name to Science.* G.P. Putnam's Sons, 1967.

Student Reading

Arnold, Caroline. *Genetics: From Mendel to Gene Splicing.* Franklin Watts, 1986.
Asimov, Isaac. *How Did We Find Out About Genes?* Walker and Company, 1983.
Bornstein, Sandy. *What Makes You What You Are?* Julian Messner, 1989.

"Hand-Me-Down" Genes

You inherit many character traits from your parents, such as eye color, hair color, and blood type. One gene comes from each parent. Many times, the gene from one parent is stronger than the other. This is called the dominant gene. The weaker gene is called recessive. Two features whose traits are controlled by gene inheritance are the fingers and the ear lobes. Discover which traits you and your family share by determining the recessive and dominant genes you inherited.

Directions: Categorize the ear lobes and fingers of members of your family by checking with grandparents, parents, uncles/aunts, brothers/sisters, or even cousins. Record your findings in the charts. Then, answer the questions at the bottom of the page.

Lobes

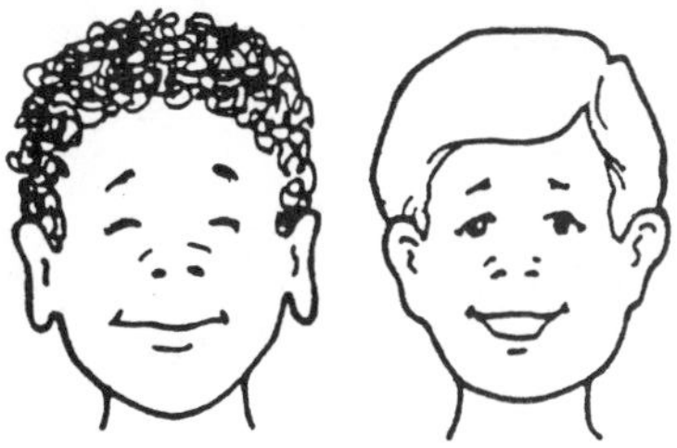

(Check the appropriate box.)

Relation to you	Free	Joined
_____	☐	☐
_____	☐	☐
_____	☐	☐
_____	☐	☐
_____	☐	☐

Free   Joined

Fingers

(Check the appropriate box.)

Relation to you	Straight	Bent
_____	☐	☐
_____	☐	☐
_____	☐	☐
_____	☐	☐
_____	☐	☐

Straight   Bent

Which seems to be dominant, free or joined lobes? _____

Which seems to be dominant, bent or straight fingers? _____

Louis Pasteur

Bacteriologist _____

Louis Pasteur was born on December 27, 1822, in Dole, France.

As a student, Louis Pasteur was not exceptional but he was meticulous and thoughtful. When he placed fifteenth among twenty-two in the entrance examination for E'cole Normale in Paris, he did not want to enter with such a low score. One year later he tried again and received the fourth highest score on the entrance exam.

While attending E'cole Normale, Pasteur studied crystals which are solids with regular, flat sides. His studies led to a new branch of science called stereochemistry, which deals with the arrangement of chemical molecules in three dimensions.

In 1856, members of a winery called on Pasteur to help them with a fermentation problem. Sometimes the process went well, but at other times the resulting alcohol soured. Pasteur studied samples of the fermenting sugar-beet juice and discovered that the yeast cells were alive, not dead as previously believed. He found a way to use heat to kill harmful microbes. This process is called pasteurization in his honor. Today the method is used to predict and preserve many foods including milk and milk products.

Next, in 1878, Pasteur set out to track down the microbe that caused chicken cholera. With much experimentation, he was able to develop a vaccination to inject in hens and protect them from disease. He turned next to combatting anthrax, a dangerous disease of cattle and sheep. With the successful production of an anthrax vaccine, Pasteur began studying rabies, the deadly disease contracted by humans when bitten by mad dogs. This study, too, was met with success.

In 1887, Pasteur suffered a stroke which affected his speech, but not his work. Twelve years later, a second stroke proved fatal. Louis Pasteur died on September 28, 1895.

Suggested Activities

1. **Grow Crystals.** Louis Pasteur spent years studying crystals. Establish that some common crystals are salt, sugar, ice, diamonds, rubies, and quartz. Students will be able to grow their own crystals in the following experiments.

Lacy Salt Crystals

Materials: 3 tablespoons (45 mL) salt; ½ cup (118 mL) water; wide-mouthed jar; black construction paper; scissors

Procedure: Pour the water into the jar and add the salt; stir. Cut a ½-inch (1.25 cm) wide strip of construction paper about half as tall as the jar. Press the strip on the inside of the jar (see diagram). Leave the jar undisturbed for three or four weeks. Observe daily.

Needle Crystals

Materials: saucer; sheet of dark colored construction paper; two tablespoons (30 mL) epsom salt; water; plastic container with lid; scissors **KIT**

Procedure: Fill the plastic container half full of water. Add the epsom salt, secure the lid, and shake vigorously sixty times. Let stand. With the scissors, cut a construction paper circle to fit inside the saucer. Pour the salt solution over the paper (be careful not to pour out any undissolved salt). Store in a warm place; wait several days.

2. **Crystallized Ink.** Students will enjoy writing messages with shiny crystals. Preheat an oven to 350 degrees Fahrenheit (180 degrees Celsius). Prepare a mixture of three teaspoons (15 mL) of salt to one-fourth cup (60 mL) of water (students may prepare their own in clean, plastic margarine cups). Dip an art brush into the saltwater and write messages on black construction paper. Be sure to stir the solution before writing each and every letter. Turn off the oven and immediately place the paper on the top rack of the oven. Remove after about five minutes.

3. **Instant Fermentation.** Add two tablespoons (30 mL) of vinegar to a glass of milk; stir and allow the mixture to sit. After a few minutes observe what happened. (Lumps, called curd, begin to form.)

Teacher References_____

Asimov, Issac. *Asimov's Biographical Encyclopedia of Science and Technology.* Doubleday & Company, 1964.
Berger, Melvin. *Famous Men of Modern Biology.* Thomas Y. Crowell, 1968.
Meadows, Jack. *The Great Scientists.* Oxford University Press, 1987.

Student Reading

Bains, Rae. *Louis Pasteur.* Troll Associates, 1985.
Greene, Carol. *Louis Pasteur: Enemy of Disease.* Children's Press, 1990.
Tames, Richard. *Louis Pasteur.* Franklin Watts, 1990.

Pasteur's Crossword Puzzle

Learn more about Louis Pasteur and his work by completing the crossword puzzle below. A word box is provided to help you.

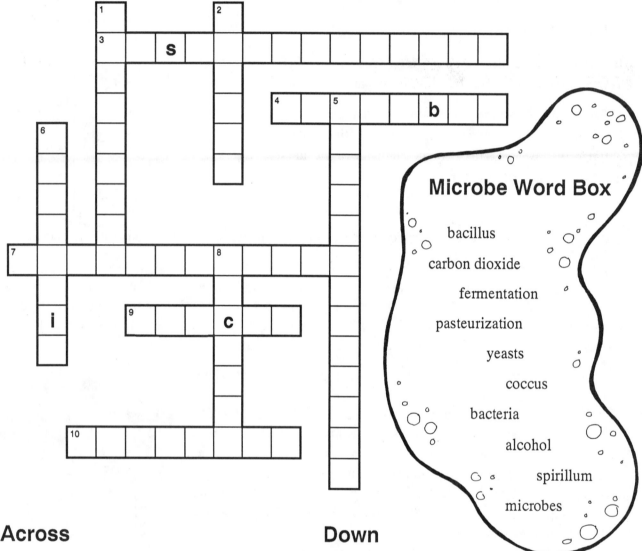

Microbe Word Box

bacillus

carbon dioxide

fermentation

pasteurization

yeasts

coccus

bacteria

alcohol

spirillum

microbes

Across

3. the heating process used to kill harmful microbes in dairy products, beer, and wine

4. organisms visible only with a microscope; some are good, some are harmful

7. process in which bubbles are formed but the substance does not get hot

9. bacteria that are shaped like spheres

10. rod-shaped bacteria

Down

1. bacteria that are spiral-shaped

2. one-celled plants that do not contain chlorophyll

5. a waste product of the fermentation process

6. single-celled microbes, some of which cause disease

8. another waste product of the fermentation process

Daniel Hale Williams

Surgeon

Daniel Hale Williams was born January 18, 1856, in Hollidaysburg, Pennsylvania. When his father died, Daniel tried his hand at several careers, including making shoes, working as a barber, and practicing law. Nothing sparked his interest, however, until he began medical training as an apprentice to a doctor. When his apprenticeship was completed, Williams attended Chicago Medical College.

Surgery interested him most. Daniel Hale Williams employed the latest methods of using carbolic acid to prevent infections in wounds and washing his hands and soaking the instruments before surgery. In 1883, he received his medical degree, set up a practice, worked on the surgical staff of South Side Dispensary, and taught at Chicago Medical College. He also began operating on some patients at home. At the time, many hospitals refused to treat African Americans. In addition, some people were afraid to enter hospitals because in the1800s that was where people went to die. Williams had a plan and on May 4, 1891, Provident Hospital and Training School opened its doors to become the country's first interracial hospital and first training school for African-American nurses.

While he was at Provident Hospital, Williams performed heart surgery on a man who had been stabbed in the chest. This was before X-rays had been invented and sophisticated, high-tech methods were available. Remarkably, the injured man lived and was still alive 20 years later. It was the first time a doctor had successfully operated on and repaired a human heart.

Dr. Williams helped establish a medical association for African-American doctors in 1895. Until his death on August 4, 1931, he also continued to practice medicine and work for equality for African-American doctors and nurses.

Suggested Activities

1. **The Working Heart.** Students will get an idea of how hard the heart works when they do this activity. Each student will need a tennis ball. Direct the students to squeeze the ball with one hand. Challenge them to squeeze it 70 times in one minute to simulate the actual pumping action of the heart. Discuss the students' reactions as you relate the simulation to the pumping action of the heart.

2. **Pulse Rates.** Make a chart like the one below for the students to copy. Divide the class into groups of two. A watch or clock with a second hand must be available. Make sure students know how to check a pulse by resting the tips of their fingers on the inside of the other person's wrist. Demonstrate this with one or two students, if necessary.

   - One partner sits quietly for 3 minutes and stays there until the other partner counts the pulse for 1 minute. (The pulse count can also be counted for 15 seconds and multiplied by 4.) Record the pulse count on the chart. Partners change places and repeat the process.

   - One partner stands for 3 minutes and stays there until the other partner counts the pulse for 1 minute. Record pulse on chart. Partners change places.

   - One partner runs in place for 2 minutes; follow above procedures.

   Have the students make summary statements about the experiments (e.g., Exercising causes the heart rate to increase.).

Name	Rest	Stand	Run
Jeri			
Anya			

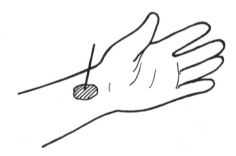

3. **Watch Your Pulse.** Give each student a toothpick and a bit of clay or play dough. Ask them how they can watch their pulse using the toothpick and clay. *Solution:* Roll and then flatten the clay or dough into a dime-size circle. Push one end of the toothpick into the dough. Press the dough into the inside of the wrist. (The clay or dough may have to be moved until a strong pulse is found.)

Teacher References

Fenderson, Lewis H. *Daniel Hale Williams, Open Heart Doctor.* McGraw-Hill, 1971.
Meriwether, L. *The Heart Man: Dr. Daniel Williams.* Prentice-Hall, 1972.
The Human Body. Teacher Created Materials #235
Big Book of Science Charts: My Body. Teacher Created Materials #570

Student Reading

Lee, George L. *Interesting People: Black American History Makers.* Ballantine Books, 1989.
Limburg, Peter. *The Story of Your Heart.* Coward, McCann, and Geoghegan, Inc.
Patterson, Lillie. *Daniel Hale Williams.* Abingdon Press, 1981.
Silverstein, Alvin and Virginia B. *Heartbeats: Your Body, Your Heart.* J.B. Lippincott, 1983.

Your Hard-Working Heart

As you read the paragraph below, notice the boldfaced words. Use these boldfaced words to label the heart diagram. An encyclopedia or science book may be used to help you.

> Your **heart** is a cone-shaped organ located in the center of your chest behind the breastbone and between the lungs. It is about the same size as your fist. The heart contains four chambers — two upper and two lower. The two upper chambers are the **right atrium** and the **left atrium**; the two lower chambers are the **right ventricle** and the **left ventricle**. Each ventricle is connected to a large artery. The right ventricle connects with the **pulmonary artery** which pumps blood to your lungs. Here the blood picks up oxygen. This oxygen-filled blood is then pumped out to the rest of your body through the **aorta** which is connected to the left ventricle.

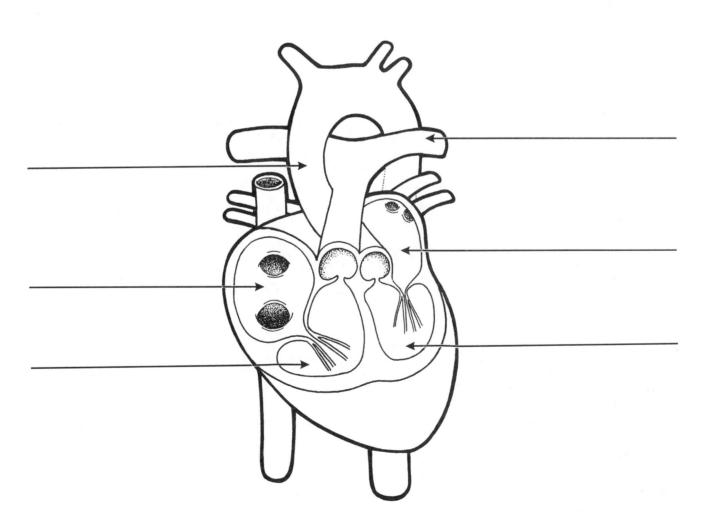

Color the left ventricle and the aorta red. Color the right ventricle and the pulmonary artery blue.

Rosalyn Yalow

Medical Researcher

Rosalyn Yalow was born on July 19, 1921, in South Bronx, an area of New York City. Her father, the son of Russian Jewish immigrants, owned a small paper and twine business.

With her parents' encouragement, Rosalyn graduated from Hunter College at the age of 19. She went on to study her favorite subject, physics, at Champaign-Urbana University of Illinois. In 1943, she married a fellow student; they had two children.

When Rosalyn pursued advanced course work in her field, she became the first female to receive an assistant's position in the physics department since 1917. During her first year in the program, she earned "A's" in every subject with an "A-" in a lab course. That prompted the department chairman to remark that her "A-" proved that women could not do well in lab work.

While working at the VA Hospital in New York, Rosalyn met her future professional partner, Solomon R. Berson. For 22 years, they investigated ways to use the new knowledge provided by nuclear physics to understand how the body functions in health and in disease. Together, they showed how radioactive iodine could be used to treat overactive thyroids and thyroid cancer. They developed the RIA method (radioimmunoassay) which is able to detect small amounts of substances in the blood including hormones, enzymes, vitamins, poison in corpses, and drugs in human hair. RIA was also useful in the diagnosis of high blood pressure, tuberculosis, and some forms of cancer.

For her ground-breaking research, Rosalyn Yalow was awarded the 1977 Nobel Prize in Physiology for Medicine.

Suggested Activities

1. **Enzymes.** One of the substances detectable through the RIA technique is enzymes. Enzymes are proteins which speed up chemical reactions. For example, saliva contains an enzyme which breaks down starches in food. To demonstrate this, give each student a soda cracker. Direct them to chew the cracker well and then to hold it in the mouth for five minutes. (Set a timer, if desired.) At the end of five minutes discuss the process. (Amylase is the enzyme at work here; it turns starch into sugar.)

2. **Viewing the Action.** Allow students to observe an enzyme in action. Two easy demonstrations are outlined below.

   • Each student pair or group will need an apple, a knife, wax paper, a spoon, and a vitamin C tablet. Direct the students to use the spoon to crush the tablet onto the wax paper. Next, have them cut an apple in half with the knife. Ask students to sprinkle the crushed vitamin C over one apple half. Allow the apple sections to sit uncovered for at least an hour. Observe both apple pieces. (Enzymes cause the untreated apple to discolor and turn brown. Vitamin C reacts with the enzymes and prevents the discoloration.)

   • Provide student groups with a raw potato slice, hydrogen peroxide, and a small plastic or paper cup. (Caution should be observed while handling hydrogen peroxide.) Have the students fill the cup one-half with hydrogen peroxide. Place the raw potato in the cup. Direct students to watch for bubbles. (Potatoes contain the enzyme catalase which causes the hydrogen peroxide to break apart into water and oxygen gas. This accounts for the bubbles.)

3. **Eat an Enzyme.** Lemon juice contains enzymes which help produce cheese when combined with milk. Each group of 3 or 4 students will need a quart of milk, the juice of one lemon, a saucepan, a strainer and cheesecloth.

   Procedure: Pour the milk into the pan and cook it over medium heat until it just begins to boil. Remove from heat and add the lemon juice. Note the milk separating into curds and whey. Pour the mixture into a strainer to catch the curds. Empty the strainer onto the cheesecloth, form a ball, and twist the cheesecloth to squeeze out all moisture. Chill.

   Spread the cheese on crackers. (Add some seasoning or salt if desired.)

Teacher References _____

Bernstein, Fred A. _The Jewish Mothers Hall of Fame._ Doubleday, 1986.

Opfell, Olga S. _The Lady Laureates._ Scarecrow Press, 1978.

Vare, Ethlie Ann and Greg Ptacek. _Mothers of Invention._ William Morrow and Company, 1988.

Student Reading

Dash, Joan. _The Triumph of Discovery: Women Scientists Who Won The Nobel Prize._ Julian Messner, 1990.

Hoyt, Marie A. _Kitchen Chemistry and Front Porch Physics._ Educational Services Press, 1983.

Van Cleave, Janis. _Janice Van Cleave's Physics for Every Kid._ John Wiley & Sons, 1991.

Vitamins for Health

The RIA technique developed by Rosalyn Yalow can be used to detect vitamins in our blood system. Vitamins are substances necessary for good health. They came from a variety of foods.

Read about each vitamin below. In the space provided, write a list of foods from that vitamin group that you eat. Share your list with the class.

Vitamin A   I Eat:

Vitamin A is needed for growth, healthy skin, bones, and
teeth. It helps the body resist infection and maintain good
vision. Food sources include: liver, kidneys, egg yolks,
tomatoes, butter, dark-green leafy vegetables, whole milk,
cheese, and deep-yellow vegetables.

_____

_____

_____

_____

Vitamin B Group: Niacin   I Eat:

Niacin can be found in poultry, meat, fish, and liver as well
as peanuts, peanut butter, potatoes, cereal, whole-grain or
enriched breads, and dark-green leafy vegetables. It is
needed for a healthy nervous system and normal digestion.

_____

_____

_____

_____

Vitamin C   I Eat:

This vitamin is needed to build the material that holds cells
together and aids in healing wounds and resisting infection.
Vitamin C can be found in citrus fruits, strawberries, to-
mato, cantaloupe, broccoli, cabbage, and raw green vegetables.

_____

_____

_____

_____

Vitamin D   I Eat:

Vitamin D can be found in fortified milk, egg yolk, liver,
herring, sardines, tuna, and salmon. It is needed for healthy
bones and sound teeth, and it also helps the body absorb
calcium and phosphorous.

_____

_____

_____

_____

Physical Scientists

Below is a listing of the physical scientists who are represented in this section. Following each name is a brief summary of related information.

Scientist	Area of Study	Country of Origin	Achievement
Jacqueline Cochran (1977-1980)	Aviation	U.S.A.	headed WASP training; first woman to break sound barrier
Marie Curie (1867-1934)	Chemistry	Poland	discovered radium; won Nobel Prizes in 1903 and 1911
Thomas Alva Edison (1847-1931)	Electricity — Invention	U.S.A.	invented electric light bulb, phonograph, movie camera
Albert Einstein (1879-1955)	Physics	Germany	wrote the Theory of Relativity; won Nobel Prize in physics
Robert Goddard (1882-1945)	Physics	U.S.A.	experimented with rockets; built a multistage rocket
Isaac Newton (1642-1727)	Physics	England	formulated the Law of Gravity and three laws of motion
Svetlana Savitskaya (1948-)	Space Exploration	Russia	became first woman to walk in space
Thales of Miletus (625-547 B.C.E.)	Physiology	Greece	became first to study forces in nature; founder of magnetism
Alessandro Volta (1745-1827)	Physics	Italy	experimented with electrical currents; built the first battery
Chien-Shiung Wu (1912-)	Nuclear Physics	China	helped disprove the Law of Parity

Jacqueline Cochran

Aviator

Jacqueline Cochran never knew who her real parents were. She was raised by foster parents in a poor sawmill town in Northern Florida. When Jackie was about eight years old (she never knew exactly how old she was), the family moved to Columbus, Georgia. There she worked 12 hours a day in a cotton mill. Her formal education lasted only two years; she learned to read and write on her own.

In her teens, Jacqueline worked in a beauty shop. A customer convinced her to study for a nursing career. She went back to the beauty business and in 1932 met her future husband, millionaire financier Floyd Odlum. When Jacqueline told him of her dream of owning a cosmetics company, he told her she'd have to learn to fly so she could transport her products quickly. Jackie loved flying and participated in many air races. After Amelia Earhart's disappearance, Jacqueline became America's number one female pilot.

With World War II on the way, Cochran pushed for a women's air auxiliary. At first, she organized a group of women to fly for England. Then the United States called her back to do the same there. Avenger Field in Sweetwater, Texas, was the training site for all U.S. female pilots. These pilots ferried planes to seaports for shipment to the fighting fronts. They tested experimental craft, new helmets, and masks. In addition to selecting and training candidates, Cochran also designed the uniforms worn by the WASPs.

After the war, Jackie set more than 200 flight records in her career. She was awarded the Legion of Merit and the Distinguished Flying Cross. In 1953, she became the first woman pilot to break the sound barrier. She wrote a book, *The Stars at Noon*, and was the first woman to land a jet on an aircraft carrier. Additionally, she was the first woman to reach a speed of Mach 2 (twice the speed of sound) and the first female to pilot a jet across the Atlantic. Jacqueline Cochran, first lady of flight, died on August 9, 1980.

Suggested Activities

1. **Flight.** Learn about some of the forces that keep a plane in flight.

   - *Thrust:* Blow up balloons and let them fly through the air. (This force pulls the plane forward and is supplied by the engine or propeller.)

   - *Lift:* Hold one end of a sheet of writing paper with the forefinger on top and the thumb and second finger underneath. Curve the paper slightly so that it does not droop. Tilt it at a slight angle keeping the opposite end higher than your hand. Hold on to the paper and push it forward. The edge opposite your hand will move up. (When a surface pushes against the jar the air pushes back. Wings provide lift.)

   - *Drag:* Take two blocks of wood with smooth surfaces and rub them together; note how the surfaces grind against one another. Now put a few drops of oil on the wood and rub them together. (This force is due to air resistance and friction which is demonstrated with the two blocks of wood.)

2. **Speed of Sound.** Sound travels at a speed of 750 miles (1250 km) per hour or 1,100 feet (330 m) per second. This is considerably slower than light, which travels at about 186,300 miles (300,000 km) per second. It also explains why you might see the puff of smoke from a starting gun at a track meet, before you hear the sound of the gun, and why lightning is seen before the crack of thunder is heard.

   Procedure: Have the students measure the speed of sound. Each student pair will need a stopwatch and a long tape measure. Measure 500 yards (450 m) and have one partner stand at the end of the 500 yards. This person should hold a rock (or other heavy object) in each hand while the other partner stands at the opposite end of the 500 yards with the stopwatch. On a given signal, the "rockholder" should bang the rocks above his/her head as loudly as possible. The partner should immediately start the watch when he/she sees the rocks strike one another. As soon as the noise from the two rocks striking one another is heard, the watch should be stopped. Record this time to the nearest tenth of a second. Repeat the experiment a few times.

   To find the speed of sound, divide the distance (500 yards) by the average time. (Have students use the recorded times from the rock activity to calculate the average time.)

Teacher References_____

Flight. Teacher Created Materials #281.
May, Charles Paul. *Women in Aeronautics.* Thomas Nelson & Sons, 1962.

Student Reading
Fisher, Marquita O. *Jacqueline Cochran: First Lady of Flight.* Garrard, 1973.
Hodgman, Ann and Rudy Djabbaroff. *Skystars: The History of Women in Aviation.* Atheneum, 1981.
Walker, Ormiston. *Experimenting With Air and Flight.* Franklin Watts, 1989.

Airplane Parts

Every part of an airplane has a special function. Some vital airplane parts and their functions are provided at the bottom of the page. Label the parts of the airplane diagram with the correct airplane part.

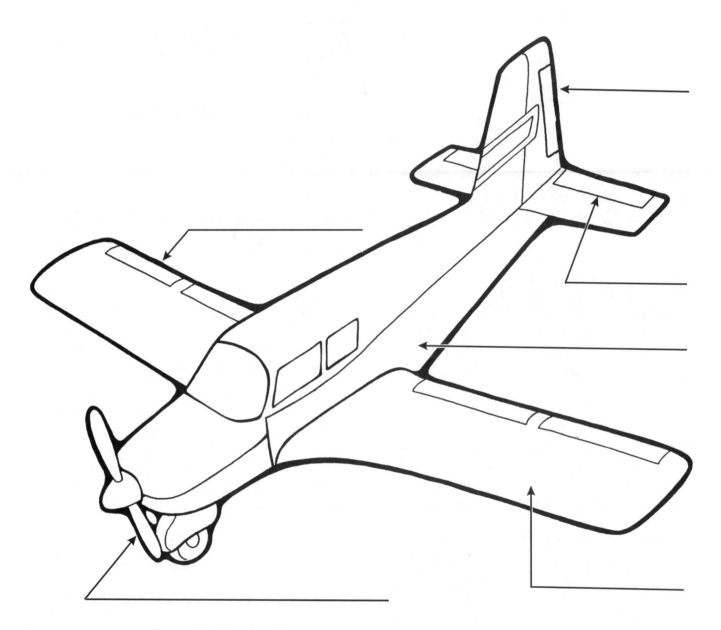

- **propeller:** pulls the plane forward so that air flows over the wings
- **wing:** provides lift when air pushes up and down against it
- **aileron:** controls banking by using a hinged strip attached to the wing
- **fuselage:** the body of the airplane
- **rudder:** located on the fin of the airplane; helps to control banking
- **elevator:** part of the tail which helps the plane pitch up or down

Marie Curie

Chemist

Marie Salomee Sklodowska was born on November 7, 1867, in Warsaw Poland. She was the youngest of five children. Higher education was not widely available to young women at the time. Marie taught herself by reading her father's math and physics textbooks. Although the University of Warsaw did not admit women, Marie was accepted at the Sorbonne in France, where she earned her master's degree in both physics and math. It was also at the Sorbonne where she met and married noted scientist Pierre Curie in 1895.

After marrying, Marie returned to the Sorbonne to pursue a doctorate degree. She became interested in the radioactive element, uranium. At the time, scientists knew the uranium was radioactive, but they could not explain why. Together Marie and Pierre set out to find an explanation. They worked with pitchblende, a radioactive ore, to remove the nonradioactive elements. That process left two radioactive elements — polonium and radium. The Curies found that radium could cure some cancers, and in 1903, they shared a Nobel Prize for the discovery of radium.

Three years later, in 1906, Pierre was killed when he was run over by a horse-drawn vehicle. Marie was offered her husband's position at the Sorbonne. She became the first woman to teach there. In 1911, Marie Curie was awarded the Nobel Prize in Chemistry, making her the first person to be awarded two Nobel Prizes.

On July 14, 1934, Marie died of leukemia caused by overexposure to radium. Her daughter, Irene, who had worked alongside her mother, also married a scientist. Together, Irene and Jean Frederic Joliot were awarded a 1935 Nobel Prize for their discovery of artificial radioisotopes.

Suggested Activities

1. **Molecular Models.** Much of Marie Curie's work involved extracting elements which are pure, single chemicals. These elements are composed of atoms or tiny particles. Atoms are joined to other atoms to form molecules. Make simple models of atoms and combine them to create a molecule.

Procedure: Prepare a dough by combining one cup (250 mL) each of flour, salt, and water. Divide the dough in half. Add red powdered tempera paint to one half; add black powdered tempera paint to the other half. Mix each batch and knead until dough is no longer sticky.

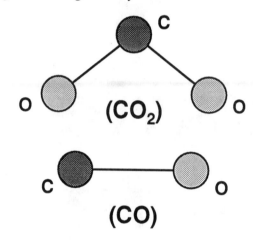

- Roll black balls to represent carbon; roll red balls to represent oxygen. (Common forms of carbon include soot, diamonds, and the lead in pencils. Oxygen is made by plants during photosynthesis. Living things breathe oxygen in order to stay alive.)

- Use two toothpicks to attach the oxygen and carbon atoms to form a carbon dioxide (CO_2) molecule. (See diagram.) Carbon dioxide is a waste product of our body.

- On another toothpick, attach one oxygen and one carbon to make carbon monoxide (CO), a poisonous substance in a car's exhaust fumes. (See diagram.)

2. **Mixing Elements.** All matter is composed of elements. These elements can be combined to form compounds. For example, when hydrogen and oxygen combine, the result is water. Have students observe some common mixing of elements.

- Dip a silver spoon into the yolk of a soft-boiled egg. Observe the black tarnish that forms on the spoon. Sulfur from the egg combines with the silver to make silver sulfide.
($S + 2 Ag = Ag_2S$)

- Bury a nail in a jar of soil; add water to the soil. Set aside, undisturbed, for a few weeks. Dig out the nail. It will have a crumbly red coating of rust. Iron atoms in the nail have joined with oxygen atoms in the jar and water to form iron oxide or rust.

Teacher References

Asimov, Isaac. *Asimov's Biographical Encyclopedia of Science and Technology.* Doubleday and Company, 1964.
Meadows, Jack. *The Great Scientists.* Oxford University Press, 1987.

Student Reading

Birch, Beverly. *Marie Curie: The Polish Scientist Who Discovered Radium and Its Life-Saving Properties.* Gareth Stevens Publishing, 1988.
Bryan, Jenny. *Health and Science: Women History Makers.* Hampstead Press, 1988.
Conner, Edwina. *Marie Curie.* The Bookwright Press, 1992.
Keller, Mollie. *Marie Curie.* Franklin Watts, 1982.

It's Elemental, My Dear

Elements are substances that cannot be broken down into simpler substances. They are the building blocks of all matter and include some substances such as polonium and radium.

When scientists talk about elements, they sometimes use symbols rather than write out the whole word. The symbols consist of a capital letter, which is usually the first letter of the element. In some cases, this first letter is followed by a lower case letter. For example, the symbol for polonium is Po; the symbol for radium is Ra.

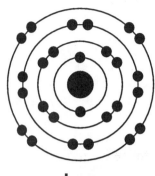

Iron

Listed below are the names of 18 common elements. Write the correct symbol next to each element on the lines provided. Use the Symbol Box to help you. A periodic chart of the elements may also be helpful. (See Vikki Cobb's *Chemically Active! Experiments You Can Do At Home.* Harper Trophy, 1985.)

Symbol Box

Au	Na	P	Al	C	Hg
Mg	Fe	U	H	Ni	I
K	Ag	Mn	Cu	S	N

1. aluminum _____

2. potassium _____

3. sodium _____

4. nickel _____

5. gold _____

6. magnesium _____

7. manganese _____

8. silver _____

9. hydrogen _____

10. phosphorus _____

11. iron _____

12. nitrogen _____

13. carbon _____

14. mercury _____

15. sulfur _____

16. copper _____

17. uranium _____

18. iodine _____

Thomas Alva Edison

Inventor_____

When Thomas Alva Edison's schoolteacher told his mother that he was "addled" (easily confused), Mrs. Edison took him out of school. Young Edison turned to books for his education. Not only could he read quickly, but he could remember almost everything he read.

After reading books on science, Thomas built a chemical laboratory in his house. When he needed money for materials, he got a job as a newspaper carrier on a train. Soon he was able to buy second-hand printing equipment and began publishing a newspaper of his own.

Next, he set up a lab in the baggage car, but an unfortunate chemical fire got him and his equipment thrown off the train. During another train accident, he was pulled to safety by his ears, which resulted in permanent damage to his hearing.

When Edison was 23, he founded the first firm of consulting engineers. For the next six years, he turned out a number of inventions. In 1876, he set up a laboratory in Menlo Park, New Jersey. This became the first industrial research laboratory. Thomas Edison's goal was to produce a new invention every ten days. During one four-year stretch he obtained 300 patents — one for every five days! In his lifetime, he patented 1,100 inventions.

Some of Edison's inventions include the phonograph, the electric light bulb, the movie camera, and the stock ticker. All of these devices have been transformed over the years into more modern, usable forms. Thanks to the genius of Thomas Alva Edison, the world has literally been transformed into a brighter place! Edison died at the age of 84 on October 18, 1931, the fifty-second anniversary of the light bulb.

Suggested Activities

1. **A Hearing Test.** When he was twelve years old, Thomas Alva Edison suffered a serious degree of deafness from an accident. This proved to be no inconvenience to Thomas, who said that his deafness helped him close out distractions and concentrate on his work.

   Students can test their hearing with the following partner activity. Each pair will need a blindfold, two pennies, and masking tape.

   - Blindfold one partner. Make sure that the ears are not covered. Have the blindfolded person sit quietly in a quiet room. The non-blindfolded partner should make a small circle with a strip of tape, sticky side out. Place a penny on one side of the tape and attach the other side to the back of the thumb.

   - Make another circle in the same manner. Attach it to the forefinger of the same hand. Click the pennies together in front of the partner; have him/her identify the location of the sound.

   - Click the pennies again directly behind and then above his/her head. (If a student seems confused, it is due to the fact that sounds coming from a spot midway between the ears reaches both ears at the same time. To locate sounds accurately, one sound should reach one ear sooner than the other.)

   - Have partners exchange roles and repeat the exercises.

2. **Thaumatropes.** The word thaumatrope means "turning miracles." These devices were toys made in the late 1800s. Certainly they were not as exciting as Edison's moving pictures, but they did provide some entertainment. Students can make a thaumatrope with the following materials: colored pencils or marking pens; a pencil; 2 four-inch (10 cm) squares of white posterboard, tagboard, or similar heavy paper; and transparent tape. **KIT**

   Procedure: Tell students to think of two things that go together (man and a hat; dog and bone.) Draw one object on one paper square; draw the other object on the remaining paper square. Tape the pencil to the back side of one picture. Tape the two pictures together back to back. Roll the pencil between both hands and observe what happens.

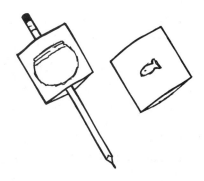

Teacher References_____

Asimov, Isaac. *Asimov's Biographical Encyclopedia of Science and Technology.* Doubleday & Company, 1964.
Electricity. Teacher Created Materials #236
Great Americans. Teacher Created Materials #112.

Student Reading

Caney, Steven. *Steven Caney's Invention Book.* Workman Publishing, 1985.
Lampton, Christopher. *Thomas Alva Edison.* Franklin Watts, 1988.
Mintz, Penny. *Thomas Edison: Inventing the Future.* Fawcett Columbine, 1989.
Mitchell, Barbara. *The Wizard of Sound: A Story About Thomas Edison.* Carolrhoda, 1991.
Sabin, Louis. *Thomas Alva Edison: Young Inventor.* Troll, 1983.
Weinberg, Michael. *What Was It Like? Thomas Edison.* Longmeadow Press, 1988.

Electric Appliances

Although Thomas Edison is credited with the invention of the electric light bulb, he invented or improved many other items which enhance our lives today. For example, Edison invented the power systems that bring electricity to homes through wires. In addition, he invented the circuits and switches that allow us to turn electricity on and off.

Imagine what your day would be like without the many electrical gadgets to which you have become accustomed. Listed below are just a few of the modern conveniences that use electricity. Write each name in the puzzle. Some clues are provided to help you get started. When you have completed the puzzle, answer the questions at the bottom of the page.

Electric Appliances

hair dryer	skillet	television	can opener
stereo	refrigerator	stove	coffee maker
telephone	computer	blender	VCR
video games	radio	clock	microwave oven

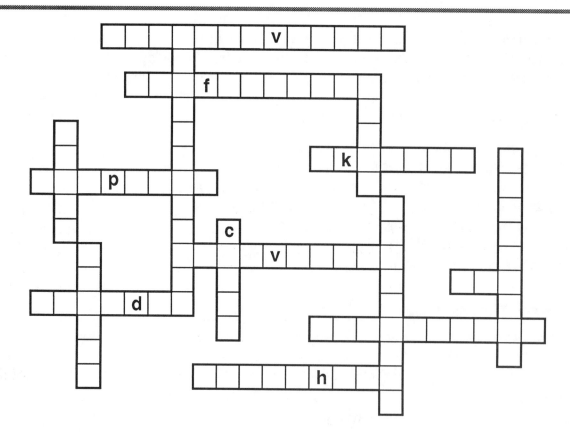

Which of these appliances do you have in your home? What is the one appliance that you cannot do without? Why? _____

_____

_____

Albert Einstein

Physicist

As a student, Albert Einstein showed little intellectual promise. He was so slow to learn verbal skills that his teachers predicted he would never be successful at anything. Albert went on to the Swiss Polytechnic Institute in Zurich, Switzerland where he was brilliant in math and physics. However, he refused to study anything else.

Nine years later, in 1905, Albert wrote five papers describing his own ideas about math and physics. Three of these papers were of major importance: one that described the photoelectric effect, a second which worked out a mathematical analysis of Brownian motion, and a third outlining the theory of relativity. By 1916, Albert Einstein had completed work on his Special Theory of Relativity and General Theory of Relativity. These theories were concerned with physical properties such as mass, energy, time, and space. Previously, scientists held that these forces were separate and could not be changed, but Einstein proved that they were related. In 1921, he received the Nobel Prize for physics.

While Einstein was visiting the United States in 1930, Hitler came to power in Germany. Since he was a Jewish pacifist, Einstein decided not to return to his homeland. Instead he set up permanent residency in Princeton, New Jersey. He became a United States citizen in 1940. Einstein accepted a position at Princeton University where he continued to work on his theories until his death on April 15, 1955.

Einstein has been described as an absent-minded man, interested only in his work, classical music, and playing the violin. His ideas, so far ahead of their time, went mostly unproven during his lifetime. Since his birth on March 14, 1879, many new advances in technology have been made which are allowing scientists to rediscover this scientific genius.

Suggested Activities

1. **Frame of Reference.** Einstein's Theory of Relativity reflects the fact that all motion is measured relative to some observer. Furthermore, Einstein said that measurements of time depend on the frame of reference of the observer.

   To help students understand the concept of frame of reference, stage an activity and position students randomly so the event is viewed from a variety of angles. For example, direct two students to run towards a finish line. Have some students view the race from the back, front, and sides of the runners. Afterwards, discuss what was seen from each point of view.

   (The x's stand for students as they watch two runners race to the finish line.)

   For a concise explanation of Einstein's theories, read David Fisher's *The Ideas of Einstein* (Holt, Rinehart and Winston, 1980).

2. **Defying Gravity.** Einstein's theories about gravity are both astounding and controversial. Here is an antigravity experiment that will amaze students. **KIT**

   Materials: strong bar magnet; clear glass (may be plastic); paper clips; thread; tape; assorted objects such as coins, plastic chips, paper, another paper clip, etc.

   Directions: Place the glass on a flat surface; lay the magnet across the top of the mouth of the glass as shown. Attach thread to one end of a paper clip. Bring the paper clip up to the magnet and allow it to stay in that position. Loosely apply a piece of tape over the free end of the thread and onto the table. Pull on the free end of the tape until the paper clip is still attracted to the magnet yet leaves a space between the paper clip and the magnet. Firmly press the tape onto the table to keep the paper clip suspended. Predict what will happen when an object is placed in the space between the paper clip and the magnet. Experiment with a variety of objects.

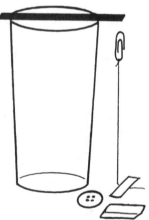

Teacher References_____

Hunter, Nigel. *Einstein*. Bookwright Press, 1987.

Kahan, Gerald. *E=mc² Picture Book of Relativity*. Tab Books, 1983.

Lightman, Alan. *Einstein's Dreams*. Pantheon Books, 1993.

Student Reading

Bradbury, Pamela Zanin. *Albert Einstein*. Little Simon, 1988.

Cwiklik, Robert. *Albert Einstein and the Theory of Relativity*. Barron's Educational Series, Inc., 1987.

Ireland, Karin. *Albert Einstein*. Silver Burdett Press, 1989.

Laurence, Santrey. *Young Albert Einstein*. Troll Associates, 1990.

Wood, Robert W. *Physics for Kids: 49 Easy Experiments with Mechanics*. TAB Books, Inc., 1989.

Square Numbers

One of the most widely recognized equations of science is $E=mc^2$. It was formulated by Albert Einstein as part of his special theory of relativity. The E stands for energy, m is for mass, and c is the velocity (speed) of light. So energy is equal to the mass times velocity squared. A number is "squared" when it is multiplied by itself. For example, if you square the numeral seven (7^2) your answer is 49 because 7 times itself is 7 x 7, or 49.

Color all the squared numbers in the box below.

1	2	3	4	5	6	7	8	9	10
11	12	13	14	15	16	17	18	19	20
21	22	23	24	25	26	27	28	29	30
31	32	33	34	35	36	37	38	39	40
41	42	43	44	45	46	47	48	49	50
51	52	53	54	55	56	57	58	59	60
61	62	63	64	65	66	67	68	69	70
71	72	73	74	75	76	77	78	79	80
81	82	83	84	85	86	87	88	89	90
91	92	93	94	95	96	97	98	99	100

Robert Goddard

Physicist _____

Robert Hutchings Goddard was born on October 5, 1882, in Worcester, Massachusetts. He was a sickly boy, but he had an avid curiosity. In 1908, he graduated from the Polytechnic Institute in Worcester, and later received graduate degrees from Clark University.

During his teenage years, he became interested in rocketry and experimented with the gunpowder rockets which were readily available then. In 1923, he tested a new type of rocket engine that used liquid fuels, gasoline, and liquid oxygen. Robert sent up his first rocket in 1926; it was four-feet (1.2 meters) high and six inches (15 cm) in diameter.

Three years later, he sent up an even larger rocket that went up higher and faster than his previous one. In addition, the rocket carried instruments — a barometer, thermometer, and camera — making it the first instrument-carrying rocket.

Due to neighbors' complaints about his noisy experiments, Goddard went to a desolate area of New Mexico to continue his work. From 1930 to 1935, he launched rockets that attained speeds of 550 miles (880 kilometers) per hour and heights of one and a half miles (2.4 kilometers). In 1914, he obtained a patent for a multi-stage rocket. Robert Goddard obtained a total of 214 patents for his new devices.

Although Goddard worked for the United States Navy developing weapons (including the bazooka gun) during World War II, the United States took little note of his accomplishments with rockets. It was not until long after his death on August 10, 1945, that the full implications of his research were realized. Today, space exploration is routine, thanks in large part to the work of Robert Goddard.

Suggested Activities

1. **Rocket Principles.** This experiment will help students understand the principle of thrust.

   Materials: hot-dog shaped balloon; bookbinding tape or masking tape; plastic drinking straw; scissors; 10 feet (3 meters) string; two chairs (or other pieces of furniture)

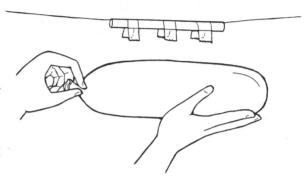

   Procedure: Thread the string through the straw. Tie each end of the string to a chair back (or other furniture piece) and move the chairs apart so that the string is taut. Attach three pieces of tape to the straw. Inflate the balloon, but just pinch it off instead of tying it at the neck. While pinching the balloon, tape it to the straw. Slide the balloon to one end of the string. Release the balloon and watch it fly across the string.

   Explanation: The thrust provided by the released air in the balloon propels the balloon forward. A rocket gets its thrust from fuels which are burned and in turn produce gases. Heat expands these gases which are pushed out of the open end of the rocket and against the closed end of the rocket.

2. **Bottle Rocket Launcher.** For this demonstration you will need to go outdoors after preparing the bottle. Be sure to stand away from the bottle until the cork launches.

   Materials: A one-quart (1 liter) soda bottle; ½ cup (118 mL) vinegar; ½ cup (118 mL) water; a cork to fit just inside the mouth of the bottle; 4-inch (10 cm) square piece of paper towel; 1 teaspoon (5 mL) baking soda; thumbtack; strips of ribbon

   Procedure Attach lengths of ribbon to the cork with a thumbtack as shown. Set aside for later use. Pour the water and the vinegar into the bottle. Put the teaspoon of baking soda in the center of the 4-inch paper towel square. Roll it up and twist the ends. (See illustration.) Go outside to complete the demonstration. Drop the wrapped paper into the bottle and fit the cork tightly into the bottle. Stand the bottle on a flat surface and wait for a reaction. (Waiting time will vary.)

   Explanation: As the water/vinegar mixture reacts with the baking soda, carbon dioxide gas is produced. Pressure in the bottle builds up as more and more gas forms. Finally the cork is forced from the bottle.

Teacher References_____

Flight. Teacher Created Materials, #281.

Richards, Norman. *Dreamers and Doers: Inventors Who Changed the World.* Macmillan, 1984.

Student Reading

Branley, Franklyn. *Rockets and Satellites.* Thomas Y Crowell, 1987.

Lampton, Christopher. *Rocketry: From Goddard to Space Travel.* Franklin Watts, 1982.

Rockets

Because of Robert Goddard's early experiments with rockets, space travel is a reality. These rockets launch spacecraft into orbit and can operate in the vacuum of outer space just as Goddard proved.

The diagram below shows the main parts of a modern rocket. Label the parts with the proper names. Use the words from the Rocket Box.

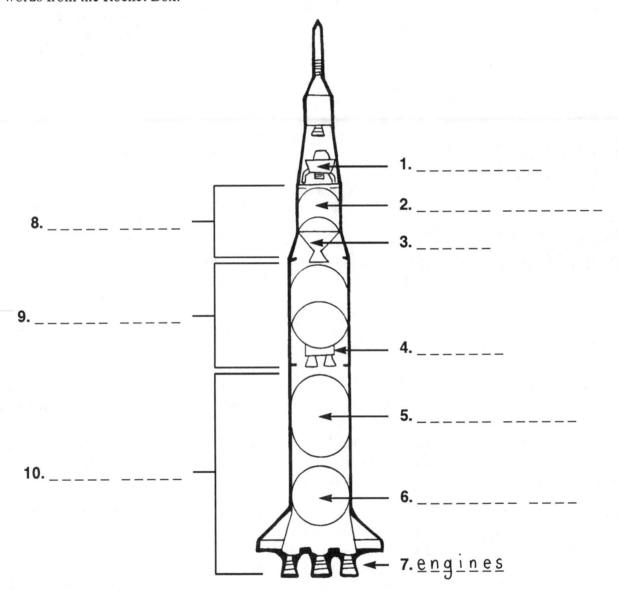

1. _ _ _ _ _ _ _ _ _ _

2. _ _ _ _ _ _ _ _ _ _ _ _

3. _ _ _ _ _ _ _

4. _ _ _ _ _ _ _

5. _ _ _ _ _ _ _ _ _ _

6. _ _ _ _ _ _ _ _ _ _

7. e n g i n e s

8. _ _ _ _ _ _ _ _ _ _

9. _ _ _ _ _ _ _ _ _ _

10. _ _ _ _ _ _ _ _ _ _

Rocket Box

second stage	spacecraft	engine
engines	first stage	liquid hydrogen
kerosene fuel	liquid oxygen	third stage

Isaac Newton

Physicist_____

Isaac Newton was born in Lincolnshire, England, on Christmas Day, 1642. His father died two months earlier and Isaac was raised mostly by his grandmother. At school, he proved to be a rather poor student but he was interested in building mechanical devices of his own design. Among the clever inventions of his youth, Newton created a windmill for grinding corn or wheat, a sundial, and a clock that was run by water power. In 1661, he entered Cambridge University. In 1669, he was appointed professor of mathematics at Cambridge.

Newton's prism experiments made him famous. He showed that white light was the combination of all colors. That was in 1666. Two years later, he invented the reflecting telescope. At about the same time, he and German scientist Liebniz, both discovered calculus.

In 1672, Newton announced the law of gravitation, which states that all objects in the universe attract all other objects with a force called gravity. Six years later, he announced the three laws of motion. In his book, *Principia*, Newton outlined, in logical sequence, the three basic laws which govern how an object moves. These laws are the principles upon which the science of rocketry are based today.

Unlike scientists before him, Isaac Newton was well-respected in his lifetime. In 1705, he was knighted by Queen Anne. When Sir Isaac Newton died in 1727, he was buried in Westminster Abbey along with England's heroes. The world owes a lot to this man who observed the simple act of a falling apple and saw much, much more.

Suggested Activities

1. **Laws in Motion.** Have the students enact Newton's three laws of motion by roller skating. Discuss the following questions and establish the law demonstrated.

   I. How did you begin moving? (Your muscles produced the force necessary to push against air resistance and to go uphill or to accelerate.) What would happen if there was no resistance or friction? (You could skate on forever.)

   First Law of Motion: A body in motion continues to move at a constant speed in a straight line unless acted upon by another force.

   II. Direct the students to push harder; what happens? (They begin to accelerate or go faster.)

   Second Law of Motion: The amount of acceleration of a body is proportional to the acting force.

   III. Explain how you got moving. (I pushed backwards against the ground. The ground pushed me forward and I began to move.)

   Third Law of Motion: Every action has an equal and opposite reaction.

2. **Get Moving.** The law of inertia states that all matter tends to remain at rest unless acted upon by an outside force. Students can demonstrate this principle with a nickel, a playing card, and a glass. Arrange the materials as shown in the diagram. Tell students to give the edge of the card a quick flick with the thumb and forefinger. If successful, the card flies away and the nickel falls into the glass.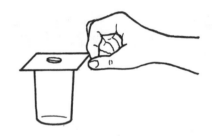

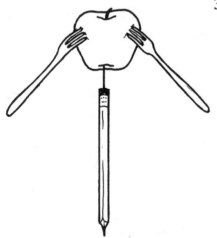

3. **Center of Gravity.** Gravity is created by the earth's pull on all bodies. In each body, these forces are concentrated at the center of gravity. If the center of gravity falls outside the base of the object, it will fall over. For example, when you walk on a balance beam, you move your arms so that you can control and keep your center of balance. Challenge students to find the center of gravity of an apple using a thick chunk of apple (or potato), two forks, and one toothpick. **KIT**

   Solution: Insert the toothpick into the apple leaving part of it outside. Push a fork on each side of the apple chunk as shown. Place a toothpick's point on top of the eraser. *Note:* If it does not balance, reinsert the fork so they hang closer to the pencil.

Teacher References _____

Cobb, Vicki. *Why Doesn't the Earth Fall Up? and Other Not Such Dumb Questions.* Lodestar, 1989.
Orii, Eiji. *Simple Science Experiments with Starting and Stopping.* Gareth Stevens, 1989.

Student Reading
Ardley, Neil. *The Science Book of Gravity.* HBJ, 1992.
Ipsen, D.C. *Isaac Newton, Reluctant Genius.* Enslow, 1985.

Your Weight in Space

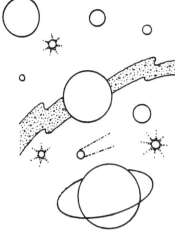

Gravity is the pull of the earth on all objects. When we weigh ourselves we are actually finding out the pull that gravity has on us.

If we were to travel to another planet or to the moon or the sun, our weight would change according to the gravity that particular heavenly body had. For example, the moon is much smaller than the earth; its gravitational pull is just one-sixth of what it is on earth. So if you weighed 60 pounds (27 kg) on earth, you would only weigh 10 pounds (4.5 kg) on the moon!

To find out what your weight would be on the sun and the other planets, complete each problem below. Assume your weight to be 60 pounds (27 kg). Write your answers on the lines provided. (Note: The answers to problems 1-9 are expressed in pounds. If using metrics, convert pounds to kilograms; then round answers to nearest kilograms.)

1. Sun (7,892 + 8,848)   _____ pounds/kilograms

2. Mercury (602 – 581)   _____ pounds/kilograms

3. Venus (911 – 859)   _____ pounds/kilograms

4. Saturn (39 + 29)   _____ pounds/kilograms

5. Jupiter (109 + 49)   _____ pounds/kilograms

6. Mars (90 – 67)   _____ pounds/kilograms

7. Uranus (39 + 25)   _____ pounds/kilograms

8. Pluto (111 – 103)   _____ pounds/kilograms

9. Neptune (302 – 217)   _____ pounds/kilograms

On the lines below, list the planets and sun in order from those having the lowest gravitational pull to those with the greatest gravitational pull.

_____

_____

Svetlana Savitskaya

Cosmonaut _____

By the time she was 15 years old, Svetlana Savitskaya had flown an airplane by herself. It was fitting that she follow in her father's footsteps, for he was an aviator and captain in the former Soviet Air Force. By the age of seventeen, she had set three world records, could fly 20 different types of planes, and had also trained as a mechanical engineer. During her training she helped design and test aircraft.

In 1975, Svetlana broke the women's speed record for powered flight. Five years later, she won a women's world aerobatics championship. All of these accomplishments helped prepare her for an achievement of a lifetime. On August 19, 1982, at the age of 34, Svetlana Savitskaya became the first woman to walk in space.

During her *Soyuz T-7* journey, Svetlana tested an arc welder outside the space station. Inside the capsule, she performed experiments in astrophysics and metallurgy (the science of separating metals from their ores). Svetlana also helped dock the *Soyuz T-7* with the *Salyut 7*, a space station that had been home to two cosmonauts since May of 1982. In 1984, Savitskaya visited *Salyut-7* again. This time she became the first woman to perform an extravehicular activity when she tested an arc welder outside the space station.

Svetlana has broken many records in her lifetime and has been instrumental in breaking the barriers to women in space.

Suggested Activities

1. **Make a Parachute.** Svetlana Savitskaya set three world records in parachute jumping. The following activity may not set any world records, but students will have fun as they experiment with the physical aspects of parachuting. **KIT**

    Materials: paper towel, handkerchief, or a piece of cloth; string; scissors; glue or tape; small weights (coins, ball of clay, fishing sinkers, washers, etc.)

    Procedure: With the scissors, cut four 12-inch (30 cm) lengths of string. Use glue or tape to attach one end of each string to a different corner of the towel (or handkerchief or cloth). Attach a weight (coin, clay, sinker, etc.) to the loose end of each string. (Perform the following steps with close adult supervision.) Hold the parachute from the center of the towel or squash the parachute in one hand before releasing it from the top of a staircase or a window. Encourage the students to experiment with different sizes and materials for the parachute body and different items to use as weights.

2. **Weightlessness.** As with all astronauts and cosmonauts whose space capsule has gone into orbit, Svetlana experienced weightlessness on her voyage. During weightlessness, objects appear to have no weight and they "float" effortlessly within the capsule. This phenomenon occurs when a spacecraft is in orbit and gravity is trying to pull the craft back to earth. The speed of the spacecraft carries it forward. As the spacecraft is being pulled by gravity and moves forward at the same time, so does the astronaut. This experiment will help students visualize weightlessness. For each group of three students, you will need thread, scissors, a glass jar, and a small doll.

Procedure: Tie a piece of thread around the neck of the doll. Tie two pieces of thread opposite each other around the mouth of the jar; connect them to the thread, holding the doll as shown.

One person holds the upper end of the thread while standing on a desk or table and releases the jar to a second person standing on the floor ready to catch it. The third person observes. Switch roles so each student can be an observer.

Teacher References_____

Bond, Peter. *Heroes in Space: From Gargarin to Challenger.* Basil Blackwell, Inc., 1987.

Cassutt, Michael. *Who's Who in Space: The First 25 Years.* G.K. Hall & Co., 1987.

Clark, Phillip. *The Soviet Manned Space Program: An Illustrated History of the Men, the Missions, and the Spacecraft.* Orion, 1988.

Student Reading

Brigg, Carole S. *Women in Space.* Lerner Publications, 1988.

Long, Kim. *The Astronaut Training Book for Kids.* Lodestar, 1990.

Newton, David E. *U.S. and Soviet Space Programs: A Comparison.* Franklin Watts, 1988.

Seymour, Simon. *How To Be a Space Scientist in Your Own Home.* Harper, 1982.

About Metals

While Svetlana Savikskaya was orbiting the Earth in *Soyuz T-7*, she performed some experiments with metals. Learn more about some common metals. Read each paragraph below. Write the name of the metal being described on the line provided. Use the Metals Box to help you. Then, complete the activity at the bottom of the page.

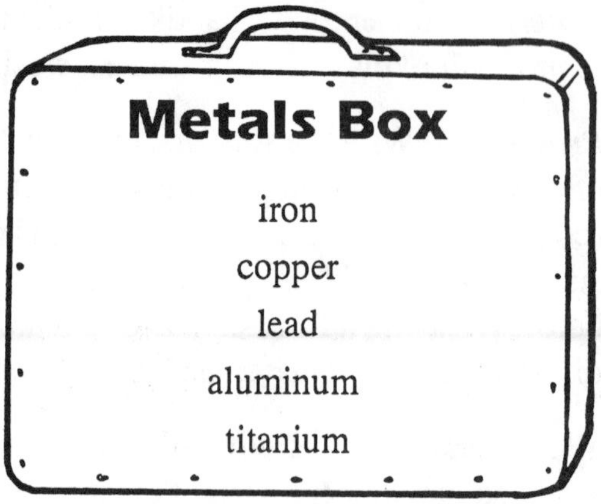

1. _____

This metal is more common than iron and composes one-twelfth of the earth's surface. It is very light and is used in everything from containers to parts for planes.

Metals Box

iron

copper

lead

aluminum

titanium

2. _____

A reddish material, it is a conductor of electricity and is used to make electrical wires. Because it doesn't rust, it is also used to make water pipes.

4. _____

This metal is as strong as steel yet weighs only half as much. It is difficult to obtain in pure form and is used in building jet engines.

3. _____

Deep inside the earth there are vast amounts of this in liquid form. On earth, it is a hard metal used to make items such as kitchen gadgets and gates.

5. _____

Even in tiny amounts this metal is poisonous to human beings, so it is no longer used to make pipes. It is also one of the heaviest and softest metals.

Look Around: Take a look around you. How many things do you see that are made of some kind of metal? Make a list of these objects on the lines below.

_____

_____

_____

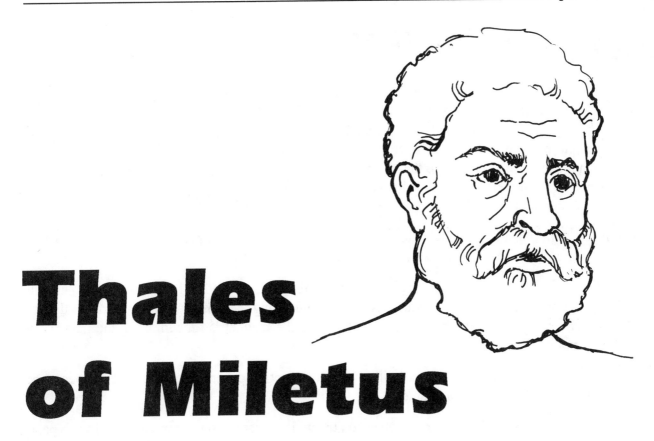

Thales of Miletus

Physiologist

Historians disagree on the exact birth year and parentage of Thales of Miletus (pronounced THAY leez of my Lee tus) but they do agree that he was a physiologist, or philosopher of nature. He was probably the world's first physiologist, as he studied various forces in nature and formulated reasonable theories about how they worked.

In the 6th century B.C., people's lives and their environment were ruled by mythical forces. They attributed changes in everything, including the weather, health, and even the outcome of war, to various gods. Thales questioned these beliefs. In his youth, he traveled to Egypt and the Near East to study the stars. Legend about Thales says that he was so absorbed in stargazing that once he fell into a ditch as he walked along, eyes focused on the stars above. It is a fact, however, that he did bring back from Egypt important information about solar eclipses. Some say that he was able to predict a total solar eclipse, but that remains doubtful since facts needed to make such a prediction were still undiscovered at that time.

Thales is credited with discovering the magnetic properties of lodestone, an ore which attracts iron. For this discovery, he has been called the founder of magnetism. One important discovery was that magnets could work through different substances. Another of Thales' achievements is his development of a theory about the earth's origin. Although he wrongly believed that the earth was flat and floated on an ocean, he set the stage for observing factual information about the physical world.

The theories introduced by Thales of Miletus showed him to be far ahead of his time. Centuries would pass before the truth about his ideas would be discovered. Thanks to this philosopher, people began to think about the world in a different way.

Suggested Activities

1. **Magnetic Attraction.** Pair or group the students. Supply each group with a magnet and a variety of materials such as bits of paper, coins, plastic disks, nails, thumbtacks, paper clips, straight pins, pebbles, etc. Direct the students to find out which materials are attracted to the magnet. Tell them to construct a chart of their findings. What can they conclude from this experiment? **KIT**

2. **Magnetic Nail.** Challenge students to magnetize a nail so that it can pick up paper clips. Provide each pair or group with a magnet, an iron nail, and some paper clips.

   Does the nail attract the paper clips? (no) Discuss how they can magnetize the nail. (Rub the nail with the magnet at least 25 times.) Ask students to try magnetizing the nail. (After some trial and error, inform students that the experiment will only work if the magnet is rubbed along the nail in one direction, not back and forth.)

3. **Dancing Bugs.** Provide each student with white construction paper, colored pencils or pen, tape, paper clips, a paper plate, and a magnet.

   Procedure: Draw and color two or three bugs on the white construction paper; cut out. Tape a paper clip to the underside of each bug. Draw a flowery scene on the paper plate. Place the bugs on the plate. Move the magnet around underneath the plate and watch the bugs move!

4. **Testing Magnetic Powers.** Thales discovered that magnets can work through some substances. In activity #3, magnets attracted objects easily through paper. Test magnetic properties with this experiment. Participants will need a glass of water, a paper clip, and a magnet. **KIT**

Procedure: Drop the paper clip into the water and wait until it rests at the bottom of the glass. Hold the magnet next to the glass as close as possible to the paper clip. Move the magnet slowly from the bottom of the glass to the top. Watch the paper clip rise. Have students conduct other experiments with magnets using a variety of materials such as a piece of plastic (lid from a container), clothing (shirt, sneakers, cap), tin can, etc. Discuss the results.

Teacher References_____

Asimov, Isaac. *Asimov's Biographical Encyclopedia of Science and Technology.* Doubleday & Company, 1964.
Meadows, Jack. *The Great Scientists.* Oxford University Press, 1987.

Student Reading

Challand, Helen. *Experiments With Magnets.* Children's Press, 1986.
Cobb, Vicki and Kathy Darling. *Bet You Can! Science Possibilities to Fool You.* Avon Books, 1983.
Edom, Helen. *Science With Magnets.* EDC Publishing, 1990.
Gay, Kathlyn. *Science in Ancient Greece.* Franklin Watts, 1988.

Opposites Attract

The three most common magnets are the horseshoe, the bar, and the "U" magnet. (See illustration.) Each magnet has two ends or poles. One pole is north and the other pole is south. If the north pole of one magnet is brought close to the south pole of another, the magnets will attract one another. Yet if the north pole of a magnet is brought close to the north pole of another, the magnets repel or push away from one another. This is stated in the law of magnets which says that like poles repel and unlike poles attract.

Directions: For this activity you will need two bar magnets. First, look at each pair of bar magnets below. Predict what will happen when a pair of bar magnets is arranged as shown. Color green the magnet pairs that will attract. Color red the pairs that will repel. Then test the predictions by experimenting with your bar magnets. How did you do?

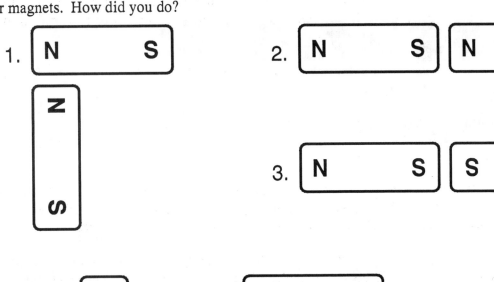

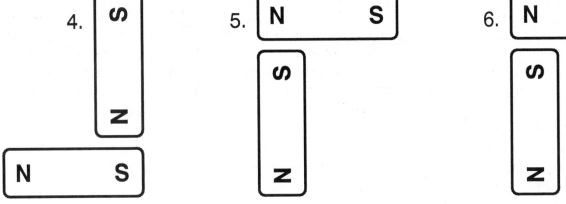

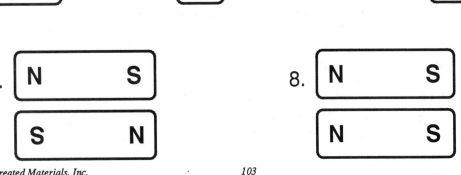

Alessandro Volta

Physicist

Because Alessandro Volta did not speak until he was four years old, his family thought that he was retarded. By the age of seven, however, he had caught up to his peers. In his adult years, he became interested in electricity. In 1775, Alessandro Volta invented the electrophorous, a charge-collecting device, which is the basis of electrical condensers still used today.

Alessandro continued his work with electricity at the University of Pavia where he received an appointment as professor. There he developed gadgets involving static electricity. He was awarded the Copley Medal of the Royal Society in 1791. He also duplicated the electrical experiments of Luigi Galvani, an anatomist who had discovered "animal electricity." But Volta questioned whether the electric current resulted when animal muscle was in contact with two metals, or if the electricity resulted from the metals alone. Further experiments proved that the presence of life or tissue had nothing to do with the electrical flow. Volta had invented the first battery!

This invention earned him a command performance to repeat his experiments for the court of French leader Napoleon Bonaparte. A number of honors followed, including the Legion of Honor and being named a count. One honor lives on today: The unit of electromotive force is called the volt.

Alessandro Volta died on March 5, 1827, in Como, Italy, the same city where he was born 82 years earlier on February 18, 1745.

Suggested Activities

1. **Flashlight Experiment.** Divide the students into small groups of three or four. Give each group a bag or box containing the disassembled parts of a flashlight. Ask the students how they can make the flashlights work. After the groups have completed the experiment, discuss in whole group how they assembled the parts to make the flashlight shine. For more of a challenge include extra and/or unnecessary parts such as a key or an extra bulb. Follow up the experiment with the activity on page 106.

2. **More on Flashlights.** Divide the students into small groups. Provide each group with a flashlight, scissors, a coin, cardboard or posterboard, and a plastic lid (from a margarine cup). Tell students to construct a chart (see sample at right). Have them cut a cardboard (or poster board) circle and a plastic circle. Predict what will happen when the cardboard is placed between the two batteries. Groups should record their response on the chart before experimenting. Afterwards, record the results on the chart. Follow the same procedure for the coin, plastic, and any other materials they might like to try. What conclusions can they draw?

Material	Prediction	Result
○ coin	will not light	did light
▱ cardboard	will light	
⬭ plastic		
⬭ paper clip		

3. **Conductors.** A conductor is a material which allows electricity to flow easily through it. Provide students with a variety of materials such as cloth, wood, paper, rocks, aluminum foil, paper clips, etc. Be sure that some will conduct electricity and some will not. Explain to students that they will be testing the materials to see which ones will light up a bulb that has been wired to a battery (i.e., which materials are good conductors). Ask students to name the materials they think are good conductors. Have student groups try the following experiment. **KIT**

Materials: 1.5 volt battery; 1.5 volt flashlight bulb; 12" (30 cm) length of insulated copper wire, stripped at both ends; electrical tape; testing materials

Procedure: Twist one end of the wire tightly around the metal base of the bulb. Securely tape the other stripped end of the wire to the bottom of the battery. To check the circuit, touch the contact point at the bottom of the bulb to the terminal at the top of the battery. One by one, place the materials to be tested between the bulb and the battery terminal. Discuss the test results. (Conductive materials will allow the bulb to light.)

Teacher References _____

Inventors and Discoverers. National Geographic Society, 1988.

Meadows, Jack. *The Great Scientists.* Oxford University Press, 1987.

Student Reading

Challand, Helen. *Experiments With Magnets,* Children's Press, 1986.

Macaulay, David. *How Things Work.* Houghton Mifflin, 1988.

Ward, Alan. *Experimenting With Batteries, Bulbs, and Wires.* Chelsea House, 1991.

Flashlight Cutaway

Label the parts of the flashlight using the cutaway diagram below.

Use the Word Box at the bottom of the page to help you.

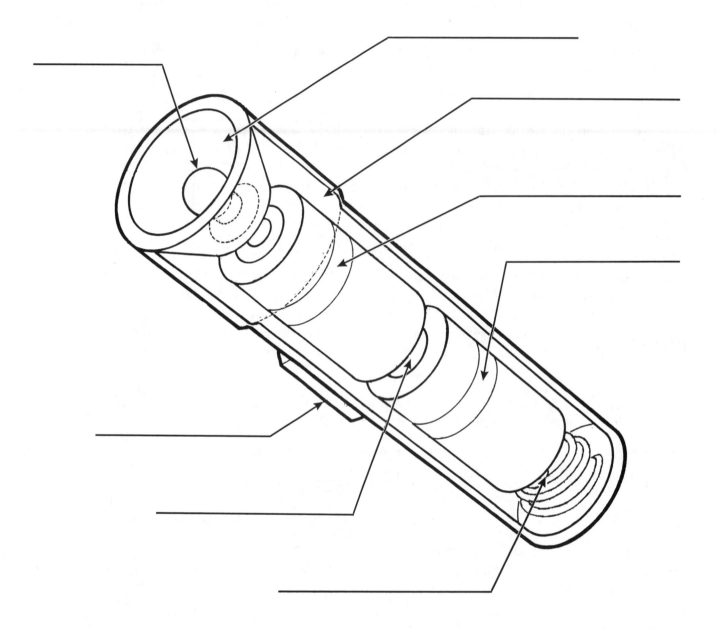

Word Box

terminal	case	battery	terminal
switch	bulb	glass	battery

Chien-Shung Wu

Nuclear Physicist _____

Dr. Chien-Shiung Wu was born in 1912, in a city near Shanghai, China. She began her physics studies there, but came to the University of California, Berkeley to complete her graduate work. At Berkeley, she studied under Dr. Ernest Lawrence, a Nobel Prize winner, who had built an atom-smashing cyclotron. Undoubtedly, Wu's parents' support of a higher education helped Chien-Shiung to reach her goals.

Known as "the queen of nuclear physics" and "the first lady of physics research," Chien-Shiung Wu is a very respected scientist in her field. She was the first woman to receive an honorary degree from Princeton University and was only the seventh woman to become a member of the National Academy of Sciences in its 100-year existence. In addition, her experiments helped two other physicists win a Nobel Prize.

Dr. Tsung Dao Lee and Dr. Chen Ning Yang were collaborating on a project to disprove the law of conservation of parity. This law states that in the nuclear world an object and its mirror image behave in the same way. Both doctors believed this was incorrect, but needed results from Chieng-Shung Wu's beta ray experiments to prove their theory. Her work did indeed support their theory, and Dr. Lee and Dr. Yang were awarded a Nobel Prize in 1957.

That was not Chien-Shiung Wu's first collaboration. Years earlier she worked on the wartime Manhattan Project at Columbia University where she developed instruments to detect radiation. The Manhattan Project was responsible for developing the atomic bomb. More recently she has worked on a project to better understand and find the cause of sickle cell anemia, a hereditary crippling disease that mainly affects black populations.

Suggested Activities

1. **Basics.** Dr. Chien-Shiung Wu's work involved extremely small particles known as molecules. Establish that all matter is composed of molecules. Molecules, in turn, are made up of atoms. To give students an understanding of what a molecule is, have them try the following activity. Each group will need sugar cubes, a magnifying glass, a glass of water, and a self-sealing plastic bag.

   Procedure: Direct the students to place a sugar cube in a plastic bag, seal it, and crush the sugar cube into its finest bits using a scissors handle, a stapler base, or some other available method.

   Examine the particles with the magnifying glass. Ask students to determine if the particles are still sugar and to explain how they arrived at their conclusions. (The small particles still contain molecules of sugar. Students can determine this by tasting.)

   Ask the students what they could do to make the particles disappear. (Dissolve them in water.) Now ask the students how they can find out if the sugar is still there. (Taste the water.) Ask students to examine the sugar water with the magnifying glass. (The dissolved sugar will be undetectable. However, the molecules of sugar, although unseen, are still present among the water molecules.)

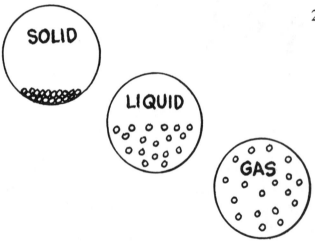

2. **Molecular Models.** To help students visualize how molecules appear in a solid, a liquid, and a gas have them construct models with paper plates, household glue, and dried peas. Direct the students to give two rows of tightly-packed peas on the bottom of one plate. Label it "solid." Label the second plate "liquid"; it should have the same number of peas only spread out across the bottom half of the plate. Plate number three should also have the same number of peas only spread out on the whole plate. Label it "gas."

   Extension: Demonstrate molecules in motion. Tell students to gently shake a zip-top plastic bag ¼ full of dried peas. Observe that the particles vibrate but stay almost in the same place. Now have them shake the bag a little harder. Watch as the peas roll over each other like molecules in a liquid. Finally, shake the bag vigorously. The peas, or molecules, continue to roll over one another even faster and may jump out of the bag if it is unzipped.

Teacher References

Gilbert, Lynn and Gaylen Moore. *Particular Passions: Talks With Women Who Have Shaped Our Times.* Crown, 1981.

Yost, Edna. *Women of Modern Science.* Greenwood Reproduction of 1959 Edition, 1984.

Student Reading

Ardley, Neil. *The Word of the Atom.* Gloucester Press, 1989.

Berger, Melvin. *Our Atomic World.* Franklin Watts, 1989.

Mebane. Robert C. and Thomas Rybolt. *Adventures With Atoms and Molecules.* Enslow, 1985.

VanCleave, Janice. *Janice VanCleave's Molecules.* John Wiley & Sons, Inc., 1993.

Atomic Numbers

All matter is composed of molecules. These molecules, in turn, are made up of atoms. Atoms are the smallest particles of matter. Within each atom is a nucleus or center. Electrons revolve around the nucleus, and are arranged in orbits. For example, an atom of lithium can be illustrated like this:

Li 3

Since there are three electrons, its atomic number is 3. Use the chart below to identify the elements pictured. Write the name of the element on the space provided.

Element	Symbol	Atomic #
Helium	He	2
Nitrogen	N	7
Oxygen	O	8
Sodium	Na	11
Aluminum	Al	13
Sulfur	S	16
Argon	Ar	18
Calcium	Ca	20

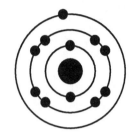

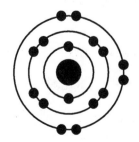

1. _____   2. _____

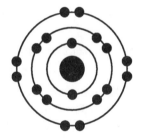

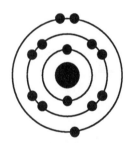

3. _____   4. _____   5. _____

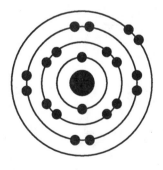

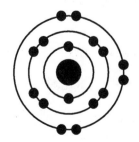

6. _____   7. _____   8. _____

Answer Key

page 13

1. Answers may vary.
   Two possibilities are:

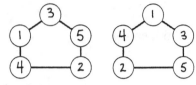

2. Answers may vary.
   Two possibilities are:

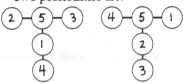

3. Answers may vary.
   One possibility is:

11	9	10
9	10	11
10	11	9

4. Answers may vary.
   One possibility is:

page 19

1. anemone
2. coral
3. eel
4. starfish
5. jellyfish
6. blue whale
7. hermit crab
8. kelp
9. squid

page 22

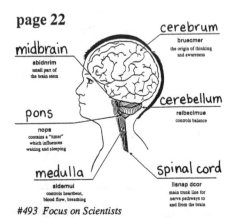

page 25

1. Mercury
2. Venus
3. Earth
4. Mars
5. Jupiter
6. Saturn
7. Uranus
8. Neptune
9. Pluto

page 28

1. hot
2. accept -20° to -25°
3. Celsius scale
4. accept 10°F to 15°F
5. cold
   (A) 18
   (B) 104
   (C) 41
   (D) 29
   (E) 37
   (F) 392

page 34

1. Petrified Forest
2. Grand Canyon
3. Grand Teton
4. Yosemite
5. Everglades
6. Hawaii Volcanoes
7. Carlsbad Caverns
8. Acadia

page 37

1. Cirrus
2. Cirrostratus
3. Altocumulus
4. Stratocumulus
5. Cumulus
6. Stratus

page 48

1. butter
2. soap
3. ink
4. cereal
5. plastics
6. paper
7. bleach
8. milk
9. dyes
10. candy
11. meat sauce
12. dried coffee

page 51

1. dwarf shark
2. whale shark
3. blue shark
4. hammerhead
5. leopard
6. carpet
7. tiger
8. great white

page 57

Chimpanzees Only:
   c, g, i, j, l, o

Both:
   a, b, e, h

Gorillas Only:
   d, f, k, m, n

page 60

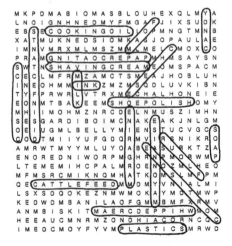

Answer Key (cont.)

page 63

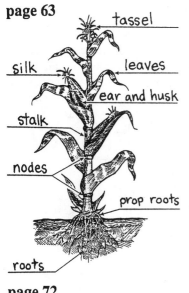

tassel, silk, leaves, ear and husk, stalk, nodes, prop roots, roots

page 72

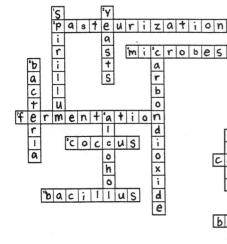

page 75

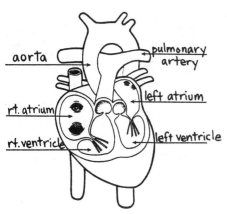

heart

aorta, pulmonary artery, rt. atrium, left atrium, rt. ventricle, left ventricle

page 82

rudder, aileron, elevator, fuselage, propeller, wing

page 85

1.	Al	7.	Mn	13.	C
2.	K	8.	Ag	14.	Hg
3.	Na	9.	H	15.	S
4.	Ni	10.	P	16.	Cu
5.	Au	11.	Fe	17.	U
6.	Mg	12.	N	18.	I

page 88

(crossword: microwaveoven, coffeemaker, skillet, computer, television, vcr, blender, videogames, telephone, stereo, hairdryer, refrigerator, clock, canopener)

page 91

Color 1,4,9,16,25,36,49,64,81,100

page 94

1. spacecraft
2. liquid hydrogen
3. engine
4. engines
5. liquid oxygen
6. kerosene fuel
7. engines
8. third stage
9. second stage
10. first stage

page 97

1. 16,740 lbs./7533 kg
2. 21 lbs./9 kg
3. 52 lbs./23 kg
4. 68 lbs./31 kg
5. 158 lbs./71 kg
6. 23 lbs./10 kg
7. 64 lbs./ 29 kg
8. 8 lbs./ 4 kg
9. 85 lbs./38 kg

Pluto, Mercury, Mars, Venus, Uranus, Saturn, Neptune, Jupiter, Sun

page 100

1. aluminum
2. copper
3. iron
4. titanium
5. lead

page 103

Color Green: 2,4,5,6,7
Color Red: 1,3,8

page 106

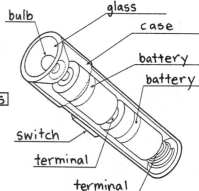

bulb, glass, case, battery, battery, switch, terminal, terminal

page 109

1. sodium
2. nitrogen
3. argon
4. aluminum
5. oxygen
6. calcium
7. helium
8. sulfur

Bibliography

Reference Materials

Asimov, Isaac. *Asimov's Biographical Encyclopedia of Science and Technology*. Doubleday and Company, 1964.

Bonta, Marcia Myers. *Women in the Field*. Texas A&M University Press, 1987.

Burne, David. *Reader's Digest: How Nature Works*. The Reader's Digest Association, Inc., 1991.

Cassidy, John. *Explorabook: A Kids' Science Museum in a Book*. Klutz Press, 1991.

Faber, Doris and Harold. *Nature and the Environment. Great Lives*. Charles Scribner's Sons, 1991.

Feldman, David. *Why Do Clocks Run Clockwise? and Other Imponderables*. Harper & Row, 1988.

Frank, Irene M. and David M. Brownstone. *Scientists and Technologists*. Facts on File, 1988.

Gardner, Robert. *Projects in Space Science*. Julian Messner, 1988.

Ingram, Jay. *Real Live Science*. Firefly Books (U.S.) Inc., 1992.

Kaner, Etta. *Sound Science*. Addison-Wesley, 1991.

Macaulay, David. *The Way Things Work*. Houghton Mifflin, 1988.

Markle, Sandra. *Science Mini-Mysteries*. Atheneum, 1988.

Meadows, Jack. *The Great Scientists*. Oxford University Press, 1987.

Reid, Struan. *The Usborne Illustrated Handbook of Invention and Discovery*. Usborne Publishing, Ltd., 1986.

Roberts, Royston M. *Serendipity. Accidental Discoveries in Science*. John Wiley & Sons, Inc., 1989.

Schwartz, Linda. *Earth Book for Kids: Activities To Help the Environment*. The Learning Works, 1990.

Spivack, Doris and Geri Blond. *Inventions and Extensions*. Incentive Publications, 1991.

Stangl, Jean. *The Tools of Science*. Dodd, Mead, & Company, 1987.

VanCleave, Janice. *Janice VanCleave's 200 Gooey, Slippery, Slimy Weird and & Fun Experiments*. John Wiley, 1992.

Periodicals

Do not overlook periodicals as an important source of scientific information. You may want to subscribe to some of the following publications for your own classroom. Check with your school, public, and college libraries to find out which of these are already available. (Reading levels are indicated within the parentheses after the periodical's name.)

Ad Astra (Advanced)
922 Pennsylvania Avenue, Southeast
Washington, DC 20078-1060

Animals Magazine (Advanced)
350 South Huntington Avenue
Boston, MA 02130

Astronomy (Advanced)
Kalmbach Publishing
1027 North 7th Street
Milwaukee, WI 53233

Chickadee (Primary)
255 Great Arrow Avenue
Buffalo, NY 14207-3082

Faces (Intermediate)
7 School Street
Petersborough, NH 03458

Kids Discover (Intermediate)
170 Fifth Avenue
New York, NY 10010

National Geographic World (Intermediate)
National Geographic Society
P.O. Box 2230
Washington, DC 20077-9955

Odyssey (Advanced)
Kalmbach Publishing
1027 North 7th Street
Milwaukee, WI 53233

Scienceland (Advanced)
501 Fifth Avenue, Suite 2108
New York, NY 10017-6102

Space World (Advanced)
P.O. Box 296
Amherst, WI 54406

3-2-1 Contact (Intermediate)
P.O. Box 51177
Boulder, CO 80322-1177